THE FUTURE IS AUTONOMOUS

THE FUTURE IS AUTONOMOUS:

THE US AND CHINA RACE TO DEVELOP THE DRIVERLESS CAR

BY PHILLIP WILCOX

NEW DEGREE PRESS

THE FUTURE IS AUTONOMOUS:

The US and China Race to Develop the Driverless Car

ISBN 978-1-63676-618-8 *Paperback*

978-1-63676-292-0 *Kindle Ebook*

978-1-63676-293-7 *Ebook*

DEDICATION

This book is dedicated to my mom, whose love and support have been invaluable both in writing this book and for my development as a person. To my father, who taught me the importance of working hard in pursuit of your passions. To Simon Radford, without whom I would not be here today because he was the one that saved me after my accident.

Thank you to everyone I interviewed for this book, some of whom have asked to remain anonymous. Your valuable insights were crucial for this book.

CONTENTS

PART 1:

INTRODUCTION TO AUTONOMOUS VEHICLES AND THEIR BENEFITS

CHAPTER 1

INTRODUCTION

Over fifty-three million Americans watched the grainy, black-and-white footage of the Apollo 11 lunar landing vessel as it landed on the moon on July 20,1969. Neil Armstrong emerged from the vessel, floated down to the moon's surface, and said one of the most famous sentences ever recorded: "That's one small step for man, one giant leap for mankind."[1]

The lunar landing occurred during one of the tensest periods of the intercontinental rivalry between the US and the Soviet Union. Both countries invested huge amounts of money in their respective space programs with the goal to send humans to the moon. The Soviet Union was the first country to send a satellite, Sputnik 1, to orbit Earth on October 4, 1957.[2] This was followed on August 19, 1960 by the Soviet Union who launched a rocket with two dogs into space. The rocket orbited the Earth for twenty-four hours before returning safely to Earth. Less than one year

1 "July 20, 1969 One Giant Leap For Mankind," *NASA*, July 20, 2019.

2 Elizabeth Hanes, "From Sputnik to Spacewalking: 7 Soviet Space Firsts," *History Stories*, Last modified August 22, 2018.

later, cosmonaut Yuri Gagarin was the first human to enter space in a Soviet Vostok Spacecraft.[3]

The Soviet Union launching Sputnik has since been referred to as the "Sputnik moment" for the US. This moment, and the following string of successes by the Soviet Union, signaled a challenge to the US. The US drastically increased the funding and focus of NASA on a mission to be the first country to send a rocket with humans to the moon. The space race between the US and the Soviet Union represented, more than anything, a battle for global technological supremacy.

Now there is a new battle between the US and China. This time, the US could lose if it doesn't get more serious about autonomous vehicles as a key technology. Driving a vehicle is one of the most complex human activities. Developing the automated driving system which can drive these vehicles safer than humans represents a monumental undertaking. Other than the vehicles themselves, the core machine learning technology which allows them to function has virtually limitless applications. The technology has already been used for things like educational aids, medical equipment, agriculture, mining, and in the military for things like drones.[4] There also needs to be policy enacted to support this effort.

A keen understanding of the political process in both countries is critical to understand the public-private partnerships which fuel new technology developments for companies in each country. Governments can spur a new technology's advancement, as in the case of China under Xi Jinping. It can also set up roadblocks that hinder its development, as in the

---

3 Ibid.

4 Asavin Wattanajantra, "AI & Automation: benefits for business & industry," *Sage*, January 7, 2019.

case of the US. I have fifteen years of experience researching and analyzing the political process in the US and how it leads to foreign and domestic policy. I also have ten years of experience researching Chinese foreign and domestic policy, US-China relations, and Mandarin Chinese.

The inability of Congress to pass a comprehensive law governing autonomous vehicles that creates uniform safety standards, the Trump administration's "tech neutral" approach to transportation management, and agency infighting threaten to grind autonomous vehicle development to a halt. Drivers are regulated at the state level in the US for things such as vehicle licensing, registration, insurance, and liability. The vehicles themselves are regulated at the national level through the Department of Transportation's Federal Motor Vehicle Safety Standards (FMVSS.) Therefore, autonomous vehicle companies would need legislation passed at two levels in order to drive on public roads.

Beyond these legislative barriers, companies need to develop new business models so autonomous vehicles will be profitable. Because of increased Research & Development (R&D) and technology costs, these vehicles cost more to develop and produce. There is also an issue of public trust in this new technology in the US. These issues still exist to a certain extent in China. However, China is able to more easily manage these issues. Because of this, China could speed ahead and win the race.

Ultimately, the need for a safer vehicular transportation system is vital. Over 1.35 million people die in traffic related accidents every year around the world. Many more people are injured. Of these accidents, an estimated ninety-four percent can be attributed to human error, such as speeding, fatigue, or drunk and distracted driving.[5] This book examines the ways in which companies in the US and China strive to create safer vehicles to make the roads a better, safer place.

In 2012, while I was studying for my PhD in the Politics and International Relations Program at the University of Southern California, I suffered near fatal injuries as the result of a fall from three stories. My spleen was severely damaged in the fall and had to be removed. Both my wrists were severely broken. Because I suffered massive head trauma, the optic nerve in my left eye was completely destroyed and there was partial damage to my right optic nerve, causing slight tunnel vision.

In my recovery process, I learned about new technological advances to help people with vision difficulties. One of these devices is the Kurzweil program which reads digital articles or books to me. This program allowed me to return to my graduate program two years after my accident to research and write my MA thesis. This allowed me to graduate with an MA in international relations. I have also been using this program to conduct research for this book.

I continue to find new ways to manage my life as someone with vision difficulties, such as scanning my surroundings closely whenever I am walking in public. This allows me to make sure that I do not fall or bump into someone. I have become reliant on public transportation. Because of this, I was unable to see my dad for six months when DC closed the metro. I take to travel to DC due to the COVID-19 pandemic. I was unable to see him, even though he only lives

---

5 *Waymo*. "2019 IAA Frankfurt Auto Show Remarks by John Krafcik." October 11, 2019. Video, 15:41.

roughly seventeen miles away. I feel blessed my injuries were not much worse, however, and that I am still alive.

Chinese companies and national and local governments have invested heavily in "New Infrastructure" projects. These projects include things like smart stoplights and roadside cameras can help autonomous vehicles communicate with the road infrastructure and other connected vehicles. This communication reduces traffic congestion and increases the vehicle's safety. Investment in China's "smart cities" is expected to reach thirty-nine billion dollars by 2023.[6]

Perhaps most importantly, the Chinese government has pushed for significant investment in 5G (Fifth Generation) high-speed wireless connection. This is highly significant because 5G connectivity offers significantly faster transmission of data from cameras and sensors in autonomous vehicles to other vehicles and the roadside cameras and smart stoplights. This gives the vehicles more time to safely avoid accidents.

Xi Jinping and premier Li Keqiang created the Made in China 2025 policy to transform China's economy by focusing on the production of new technology. This puts China in direct competition with the US because the US has dominated the global high-tech market for decades. Xi can create national standards, albeit with some regional variations, much faster than President Trump can in the US

I believe right now the US is beating itself. The Trump administration promised to massively increase investment in the US's aging and occasionally unsafe transportation

---

6 "Investment in China's smart cities to approach $39b by 2023," *China Daily*, July 14, 2019.

infrastructure. Instead, the Trump administration has proposed budget cuts to the Department of Transportation's (DoT) discretionary funding as high as 21.5 percent in its 2020 proposed budget.[7]

Some of this discretionary money goes to smart infrastructure projects and companies, universities, and other research organizations testing autonomous vehicles. These groups test vehicle to infrastructure (V2X) applications and run pilot shared autonomous vehicle (SAV) shuttles and vehicle simulations.[8]

The lack of spending on basic infrastructure endangers people in both conventional and autonomous vehicles. Problems are not only limited to US domestic policy. The ongoing trade and security dilemmas create tension between the two largest economies in China and the US. This tension will complicate efforts to establish uniform global standards for things like the safety of these vehicles.

This is not another Cold War. However, the relationship between the US and China is at its lowest point in decades. This political tension must be taken into consideration when analyzing the race to develop autonomous vehicles. Because the supply chain is global, autonomous vehicle companies in both countries have been negatively impacted by the tariffs on goods and services imposed by the governments of both countries.

This book is for people interested in new technologies such as the autonomous vehicle, which has the potential to revolutionize the transportation system. Policymakers and

---

7 Michael Laris, "Trump administration proposed billions in transportation cuts – and new spending," *The Washington Post, February 10, 2020.*

8 Eva Fox, "Education and Experience Will Help Americans Trust Self-Driving Cars," *Tesmanian, May 20, 2020.*

people interested in US and Chinese policy will also like this book. Autonomous vehicles have economic, technological, legal, and security implications to be addressed for both countries. This book examines all of these challenges and how each country seeks to manage them.

This book is divided into four parts. Part one introduces the potential benefits of autonomous vehicles, the pushback they have received, and describes the automated driving technology driving them. Part two describes the technological and business-related challenges of major autonomous vehicle companies in the US. Part three analyzes the efforts by Xi Jinping and the Chinese government to transform China's economy, the impact of the trade and security dilemmas between China and the US and introduces key companies in China's autonomous vehicle industry. Part four describes the policies needed in the US for the autonomous vehicle industry to succeed and concludes with a look toward the future.

After recovering from my injuries, I became passionate about finding out more and advocating for autonomous vehicles. They could give me and millions of other blind, disabled, or elderly people greater transportation freedom. In my research, I discovered their other commercial and safety benefits. I sincerely hope you will join me in advocating for this vital technology after reading this book.

CHAPTER 2

FOR AUTONOMOUS VEHICLES, NECESSITY IS THE MOTHER OF INVENTION

THE INCREDIBLE BENEFITS OF AUTONOMOUS VEHICLES IN THE US

Imagine a situation in which a man wakes up to his alarm crowing like a rooster. He stumbles out of bed and enters his bathroom to take a shower. While he sits down for breakfast, he gets an alert from an app on his cell phone. The autonomous vehicle has arrived at his house with his dry cleaning. He leaves his house, gives the driverless vehicle a thumbs up to open the trunk, takes out the package with his suit and button-up shirts, gives the vehicle another thumbs up to close the trunk, and returns to his house. He then walks to his bedroom and hangs the clothes in his closet. Recognizing it is time to head to work, he uses another app on his phone to order a shared autonomous vehicle to pick him up.

Five minutes later, he receives another alert from Uber saying his vehicle has arrived. He gulps down the rest of his coffee and walks outside. The door of the van slides open, allowing him to enter. He climbs inside and sits next to a blind man wearing sunglasses with his service dog sitting attentively on the floor in front of him. The van doors automatically close behind him and the van starts driving toward his destination.

He pulls out his computer, connects to the van's Wi-Fi network, and starts responding to emails to begin his work for the day. On the commute, he glances out the window to see the clear blue sky and the van passes a park filled with lush green trees and shrubs. There is a young girl swinging on a swing set in a playground, pushed by her mother. He recalled when there used to be an ugly multilevel parking lot where the park is now. After about thirty minutes on a commute which previously took over forty-five minutes, the van arrives at the stop near his office. Several other autonomous vehicles speed off in different directions with no need for traffic lights or stop signs. He was ready for a productive day at the office.

* * *

This situation reflects what both the US and China are striving for: a situation in which shared autonomous vehicles reduce traffic congestion by having fewer vehicles on the road. There would no longer need to be stoplights or stop signs if the autonomous vehicles accounted for the majority of the vehicles on the road.

Furthermore, an estimated thirty percent of the carbon dioxide and other harmful emissions produced in the US alone come from vehicle exhaust. According to renowned autonomous vehicle advocate Brad Templeton's website, this figure could be reduced by as much as twelve to fifteen percent. This would be the case if personal car ownership was replaced by shared rides in autonomous "robotaxi" fleets.[9]

Plans and some initial progress to develop the autonomous vehicle industry have already begun. However, there has been pushback from certain groups that would lose their jobs in the short term. The job losses from people who work as taxi drivers, truck drivers, and delivery vehicle drivers would need to be addressed through job retraining programs or other job creation platforms. These problems will be addressed in greater detail in other chapters in this book but continued stagnation on the US policy front with failure to pass a law governing autonomous vehicles by Congress could stall their development and defer the above scenario.

According to INRIX's 2019 Global Traffic Scorecard, people in the US spent ninety-nine hours on average per year commuting to and from work. Because of this almost one hundred hours of lost work productivity, people lose an average of $1,377.[10] This is not to mention the incredible stress of driving to work, especially in places like New York City in the US or Beijing in China. This stress caused by driving in traffic congestion can lead to health risks, such as a greater risk for strokes or heart attacks.

I mentioned the bone-chilling statistics of over 1.35 million people dying in traffic fatalities all over the world due to traffic accidents in the introduction. These accidents

---

9 Brad Templeton, "Where Robot Cars (Robocars) Can Really Take Us," *Bra Templeton's Home Page.*

10 Press Release, "INRIX: Congestion Costs Each American Nearly 100 Hours, $1,400 a year," *INRIX*, March 9, 2020.

particularly affect young people. Traffic and other accidents are the leading cause of death for people ages fifteen to nineteen.[11] The vehicle transit system needs to change. That is why there is urgent competition to develop autonomous vehicles and is why the outcome of who perfects this technology first is critical. The country, or group of countries, who develops the technology first will strive to create the global standards. This will also allow that country to gain an advantage in the potential trillion-dollar industry for autonomous vehicles.

Many of the benefits of autonomous vehicles presuppose people in the US will choose to ride in a shared "robotaxi." This might be a difficult transition to make. People in the US have been owning and driving their own vehicles for more than one hundred years.

I spoke with Dr. Yochanan Bigman, postdoctoral research fellow at University of North Carolina Chapel Hill. His research focuses on issues of machines making moral decisions. He said in his interview, "I think it might make people a bit slower in adopting this new technology, but I don't think it's a big barrier." He continued to say, "I think if people see the benefits, if we have these traffic jams, and we don't need to worry about parking, and people that die in accidents, and insurance costs will be lower." Dr. Bigman agreed acceptance might be lower because of the entrenched driving culture in the US. In the end, he feels the benefits of shared rides in autonomous vehicles would win people over.

The question of safety is of primary importance for all of the different autonomous vehicle companies I discuss in this book. Researchers have found drivers are rarely blamed for

---

11 "National Center for Health Statistics," *The Center for Disease Control and* Prevention, 2017.

accidents which kill pedestrians or cyclists. The articles in newspapers also rarely mention the large number of people killed in these accidents as a public health crisis. The study was conducted by researchers from Rutgers University, Arizona State University, and Texas A&M University. The article appeared in a journal of the National Academy of Sciences' Transportation Research Board.

The study analyzed four thousand articles reporting deaths to pedestrians and cyclists and two hundred were chosen as a sample from February and March 2018. Of these articles, one hundred were related to deaths of pedestrians hit by a vehicle and the other one hundred involve vehicles and cyclists. According to the authors of the article, "Coverage almost always obscures the public health nature of the problem by treating crashes as isolated incidents, by referring to crashes as accidents."[12] This study presents disheartening news for the autonomous vehicle industry. Companies in the industry emphasize the potential safety benefits of their vehicles, whereas this study indicates the media downplays the public health crisis of vehicle fatalities.[13]

An Uber autonomous SUV struck and killed Elaine Herzberg as she was crossing the street in Tempe, Arizona on March 18, 2018.[14] The accident, which I will discuss in my chapter on Uber later in this book, made headlines and appeared in frequent news stories on 24/7 news outlets in the US. Elon Musk, CEO of Tesla, frequently states in speeches

12 Richard Florida, "How Media Coverage of Car Crashes Downplays the Role of Driver," *Bloomberg CityLab*, December 10, 2019.

13 Richard Florida, How Media Coverage of Car Crashes Downplays the Role of Driver," *Bloomberg CityLab*, December 10, 2019.

14 Daisuke Wakabayashi, "Self-Driving Uber Car Kills Pedestrian in Arizona, Where Robots Roam," *The New York Times*, March 19, 2018.

and tweets there is an inherent bias against autonomous vehicles by the media in the US. They are also held to a higher standard of safety than conventional, human-driven vehicles. While this may be true, work still needs to be done to improve the safety of autonomous vehicles because the technology is still relatively new.

Autonomous vehicles, when the technology is fully mature, offer several commercial applications as well. Commercial applications for autonomous vehicles have already been adopted by companies to solve specific problems in the US. These problems include the desire by many people to have contactless delivery of groceries, food, or other goods to avoid catching the coronavirus during the COVID-19 pandemic, and to assist with the long-haul freight trucking industry to support the logistical supply chain. The logistical supply chain is the lifeblood of the US economy and is experiencing driver shortages for this crucial means of delivering goods across the country as safely and efficiently as possible.

Disruptive technologies, such as the autonomous vehicle, are technologies with the potential to change many industries, sometimes drastically. As the name suggests, this disruption will affect different people in different ways. Government policies for job retraining will be necessary for people who will lose their jobs in the short term. The agreement by a large percentage of people to adopt shared vehicle rides will be crucial. This chapter describes some key technological concepts related to autonomous vehicles helpful in understanding exactly what these vehicles are and how they work. This chapter then describes the benefits autonomous vehicles can bring people and the sacrifices necessary for these benefits to be felt on a large scale.

UNDERSTANDING THE BASICS BEHIND AUTONOMY

Several basic concepts are helpful to understand to get a better understanding of autonomy in general. Autonomy means an AI device does not need help from people to complete a task or set of tasks. Autonomous vehicles demonstrate autonomy to a degree depending on their level of automation. The different levels of automation are determined by standards created by the Society for Automotive Engineering (SAE). These standards are used by the National Highway Traffic Safety Administration (NHTSA). NHTSA has broad authority and creates the Federal Motor Vehicle Safety Standards (FMVSS) in the US.[15]

Many people already own a level one automation vehicle if it was purchased in the last ten years. Level one vehicles have very basic autonomous functions such as Anti-lock Braking Systems (ABS) and adaptive cruise control features that can accelerate or brake when driving.

Level two vehicles have things like steering and lane-keep assist, and the vehicle itself can drive. However, under level two the vehicle does not monitor the road and the driver is responsible for paying attention to the road and taking control. This is what Tesla vehicles are officially ranked while driving with autopilot engaged. If autonomous trucks are driving in a platoon and closely following a human-driven truck, then that would also be level two.[16]

At level three, the vehicle itself monitors the road and controls the braking, acceleration, and all other driving functions. Traffic jam assist would also be considered level three. The driver does not need to monitor the road. The vehicle

15 Melanie May, "The 6 levels of self-driving car – and what they mean for motorists," TheJournal.ie, September 18, 2017.

16 Ibid.

will issue a "takeover warning" to the driver to take control. At that point, it would be the driver's responsibility if there is an accident.[17]

At level four and five autonomy, the vehicle controls all of the driving functions by itself. This includes accelerating, braking, signaling and changing lanes, turning, and responding to hazards on the road. These hazards could include avoiding pedestrians as they cross the road, other vehicles, or other objects. At level four autonomy, the vehicle must already have a high-definition static map of the roads. The map is located in the cloud, which allows it to be updated remotely. At level five, the vehicle drives autonomously at all times, in all places, in any weather conditions, and does not require human intervention.[18]

Brian Jee, an autonomous vehicle technical program manager, confirmed, "Mapping is just brutal." He continued by saying a vehicle, with all of the cameras and sensors, would have to frequently drive down roads in a planned and coordinated process to ensure data quality and redundancy. Onboard cameras and sensors record millimeter-accurate data of everything on or near the road from the car's perspective. The resulting map is called the delta, a high-definition (HD) map or, as engineers refer to them, semantic and geometric maps.

The mapping process is repeated multiple times through each lane, in addition to each direction of traffic. Not only does this take a long time, but it is also very expensive. It can cost $2,000 per linear kilometer. The maps also need to be constantly updated because the world changes. Someone

---

17 Ibid.

18 Ibid.

could have graffitied a sign or there could be a new construction project. The difference between the real world and the mapped world is known as a delta. The expensive mapping process needs to be repeated every time a delta or map data issue is identified.

Because these maps must be constantly updated, how exactly will these updates be downloaded to the vehicle's cloud computing system? One option would be through connection to a home Wi-Fi network. However, another option would be through connection to a wireless network. Jee described the importance of a Fifth Generation (5G) wireless network connection for autonomous vehicles. He said a 5G network assists autonomous vehicles in several ways. He said, "5G is the access (of the vehicle) to the rest of the world." Because the different systems are computing at the edge of the internet or edge of what computer processing will allow, it needs a connection back to the server architecture. Therefore, a 5G network unlocks a lot of bottlenecks for the vehicle to drive safely.

For instance, Mr. Jee discussed how Tesla pioneered the Over-the-Air (OTA) updates system. This system will be described in my chapter on Tesla. When you're at home, the car can connect to Wi-Fi and download the update. According to Mr. Jee, "These updates will be more often and more significant. There will be huge changes to the deep learning models." Continuing with the example of Tesla, Mr. Jee admitted the system had trouble recognizing traffic cones. With a 5G network connection, the vehicle could use the OTA updates system to more rapidly download a perception update so your car could recognize traffic cones and drive more safely.

The greater speed and capacity of the network would also allow for someone in an office to monitor the state of the vehicles remotely. This would be done either by autonomous vehicle companies themselves or they could license this task to a third party. Mr. Jee said, "If there's a dispatcher monitoring how the car's doing, monitoring any errors, or when the car gets stuck and doesn't know what to do and it just stops in the middle of an intersection, then you're going to be in trouble." While this scenario sounds frightening, he assured me a 5G network connection would allow for a more robust and lower latency teleoperations person to recognize the problem and a remote technician to fix the problem and prevent a potential accident.

I will describe the autonomous vehicle technology in greater detail in chapter five. However, this general information about the autonomous vehicle technology is helpful to understand both the capabilities and current limitations of these vehicles for the rest of the book.

POSSIBLE INITIAL DEPLOYMENT SUCCESS STORIES FOR AUTONOMOUS VEHICLES

The scenario I described to introduce this chapter sounds too good to be true. Where's the catch? All of those new products and services sound like they would be at least ten years in the future, if not more.

This is both true and false. The truth is yes, some may be ten or more years in the future. However, some benefits have already been realized by people. Every new technology gets better over time. New developments are hard to predict, and this impacts when autonomous vehicles will be ready for large-scale deployment. With a potentially disruptive technology like the autonomous vehicle, the degree to which it penetrates society is also hard to predict. So much is still unknown about the capabilities of autonomous vehicles. So much also depends on laws that will either accelerate or delay the development and deployment of autonomous vehicles. Or there could be a situation like there is now in the US of creating roadblocks for the production and deployment of these vehicles. Several applications of autonomous vehicles could be ready to deploy on a limited scale now or in the near future.

According to a July 2018 report by KPMG, investment in artificial intelligence (AI) and robotic process automation (RPA) is currently at $12.4 billion. However, it is expected to increase to $232 billion by 2025. This staggering increase in funds for AI and RPA can largely be attributed to companies attempting to retain their current value during the economic downturn brought on by the COVID-19 pandemic.[19]

One thing is clear. Even after the economic downturn is over, there will be no going back to "business as usual." Companies that learn to adopt automation into their business will thrive. Those that cannot will likely fail.

Automated systems, such as robots that clean the floor and stock shelves in stores, can both add efficiency to this process and increase people's trust in autonomous technology. Robots operating in enclosed spaces like universities or short-distance delivery robots on sidewalks can offer nearly contactless delivery. This will allow for less risk of viral transmission during the current COVID-19 pandemic.

The world's largest retail store, Walmart, is using robots to perform many different tasks. These tasks include scrubbing the floors, scanning boxes, unloading boxes from trucks, and

---

19 Michael Moore, "AI investment will hit $232 billion by 2025," *ITProPortal*, July 31, 2018.

tracking shelf inventory. While labor groups complain this could cost people jobs, Walmart maintains staff will still be needed to assist customers. According to an article published by *BBC News* on April 19, 2020, people were apprehensive about these robot cleaners and scanner robots at Walmart stores in the US at first, preferring "a human element."[20]

I talked with author David Kerrigan, author of *Life as a Passenger: How Driverless Cars Will Change the World,* about near-term use cases for autonomy. During our conversation, he mentioned the Walmart example as a positive example, saying, "So I think those simple environments, where you can have the cleaning and the stock taking robots operating when the store is closed will be acceptable to consumers." He then described how Walmart has started using the cleaning robots when the store is open. He described people's reaction to these robots, saying, "Because of the positive effect on consumer's perception of hygiene. Previously they didn't want the robots to be visible but now consumers are actually pleased to see the robots cleaning," which helps with hygiene. Perceptions of robots who operate in similar ways to autonomous vehicles will also be helpful for changing the public's perception of autonomous vehicles.

Dave Ferguson and Jiajun Zhu, who both worked on Google's self-driving car project (now Waymo), left Google in 2016 and founded Nuro. Nuro focuses on short-distance delivery of goods. Their website promises customers can "Get anything, anytime, anywhere." With no driver and an open space to retrieve items a person orders ahead of time, there is minimal risk of person-to-person transmission of a virus.

---

20 Drew Harwell, "As Walmart turns to robots, it's the human workers who feel like machines," *The Washington Post*, June 6, 2019.

This service presents an ideal solution to the current COVID-19 pandemic for food and other delivery options.[21]

As discussed in the hypothetical introduced this chapter, Nuro created a system for its vehicles in which a person only needs to give a thumbs up to open and close the compartments containing their items. Nuro is also using vehicles from its autonomous vehicle delivery fleet to assist two field hospitals in California. The vehicles deliver medical supplies to healthcare workers working in the two stadiums that have been converted to hospitals to deal with patients infected with COVID-19.[22]

Walmart has also created a pilot program with Nuro to deploy autonomous delivery trucks. In this pilot plan, Nuro vehicles will deliver groceries from a Walmart location in Houston, Texas.[23] This deal between Nuro and Walmart represents a key first step in what could be a massive increase in the efficiency of the long-haul freight trucking industry in the US.

I talked with Karolina Chachulska, who is the director for customer experience and growth at Info Edge. She has experience identifying near-term use cases for autonomous vehicles. She mentioned it is a very good time for Nuro to focus on grocery delivery during the COVID-19 pandemic.

However, she cautioned Nuro and small delivery robot company Starship "still [are] not fully contactless. We still need to think of how to make it fully contactless." She then discussed companies, such as Postmates and Starship, that

---

21 "Delivering the future of local commerce, autonomously," *Nuro*, 2016.

22 Andrew J. Hawkins, "Nuro is using driverless robots to help health-care workers fighting COVID-19," *The Verge*, April 22, 2020.

23 Peter Holley, "Walmart teams with Nuro's robot cars to deliver groceries in Houston, *The Washington Post*, December 11, 2019.

can drive on sidewalks. These robots still need to be controlled through a teleoperations system. She said, "Most frequently, the people are sitting hundreds, or thousands, of miles away from a delivery." Because this process relies on teleoperation, she mentioned it relies on one absolutely critical point: connectivity. If Starship or Postmates robots do not have access to wireless data, the whole system shuts down.

People appreciate the convenience of having groceries, food, and other goods delivered to their homes, whether it is delivered through autonomous vehicles like Nuro, by Starship or Postmates robots, or delivery vehicles driven by humans. This trend has expanded in popularity during the COVID-19 pandemic and is likely to continue, even after the pandemic goes away.

AUTONOMOUS TRUCKS SUPPORTING THE SUPPLY CHAIN "LIFEBLOOD" OF AMERICAN INDUSTRY

Nearly contactless delivery represents a key benefit for delivery of goods to people, and the delivery of goods by freight trucks represents a massive need for autonomy to fill. According to the Bureau of Labor Statistics' (BLS) 2018 study, trucks transport seventy percent of the goods in the US. This is far greater than the amount of goods transported by boat, train, or plane.[24]

Driver retirement is also a concern because the average age for a truck driver in the US is fifty-five years old. There are many drivers in their sixties and seventies. The lack of drivers, coupled with consumer demand for more goods to be transported to more places as fast as possible, means there

24 Steven John, "11 incredible facts about the $700 billion U.S. trucking industry," *Business Insider*, June 3, 2019.

could be a shortage of up to one million trucks in the near term.[25] There is a vital need for autonomy to ease some of the burden for this critical industry by providing autonomous trucks to keep the US's economy running smoothly.

The logistical transport system supply chain, or the system by which goods are transported from factories or ports to distribution centers to people's houses, serves as the lifeblood of the American economy. Virind Gujral is the Founder of Transformation to Intelligent Automation (T2Ia). He has worked in the logistics supply chain in the US for over thirty years. He described how automation can benefit the logistics system. He explained, "Whatever we manufacture we need to get the ingredients to the production areas, and once it has been produced to send it to the distribution centers and from distribution centers to individual homes."

Gujral stated this supply chain operates very efficiently in the US. It is vital to our day-to-day operations as a country. He is in favor of introducing autonomous trucks because he says, "There is always room for more improvement and with the volume so high, a small amount of improvement goes to millions and billions of dollars." As described above, this vital logistics system may need automation just to keep at its current rate of efficiency sooner rather than later.

There has been substantial interest in autonomous trucking by autonomous vehicle companies in recent years. Leading autonomous vehicle company Waymo's CEO John Krafcik described the importance of this trend toward delivering goods to people in an online article from Reuters. According to Krafcik, "The reality right now is that goods

---

25 Samantha Raphelson, "Trucking Industry Struggles With Growing Driver Shortage," *Here & Now Compass*, January 9, 2018.

delivery is a bigger market than moving people." Waymo, which will be featured in another chapter in this book, previously focused on establishing a fleet of autonomous taxis. While it has not abandoned this goal, it recently signed pilot program deals with UPS and Walmart for goods delivery in its fleet of trucks. It calls these trucks Waymo Via.[26]

In the last seven months from when the article was published in May 2020, investors gave six billion dollars in funds to over two dozen goods and grocery delivery companies. These included companies with everything from delivery drones, sidewalk delivery robots, other delivery vehicles, and even long-haul freight trucks. Companies like Waymo recognized the need to assist the freight sector in the US and were quick to capitalize on that opportunity.[27]

Companies' urgency to jump on an opportunity to generate money in the long-haul trucking industry is great, but wouldn't this lead to mass layoffs of truck drivers?

As mentioned above, there is an opening in the trucking industry because many divers have retired or will likely retire soon. Even though automation for freight trucks is easier than for vehicles in crowded city streets, researchers at MIT released a study describing the future of automation in trucking as a mixture of human and automated trucks. There would be a platoon of trucks, they argue, led by a truck drive by a human and followed closely by several autonomous trucks.[28]

---

26 "Autonomous vehicles cash in on coronavirus-driven demand," *hpauto*, May 18,2020.

27 Ibid.

28 SCDigest Editorial Staff, "Supply Chain News: MIT Report Says not to Expect Self-Driving Trucks any Time Soon," *Supply Chain Digest*, July 28, 2020.

While the authors of the study argue this would not have a drastic impact on the industry, there would likely not be safety operators in these autonomous trucks. They also argued they did not anticipate autonomous vehicles to be widespread in more than just a limited area of operation within the next ten years. With the effect spread over a period of ten or more years, it is more likely the truck drivers, and the industry in general, would be able to adapt to these changes.[29]

Autonomous vehicles represent a potentially revolutionary change in the transit system. As with all revolutions, there will be winners and losers in the short and long term. Industry leaders and analysts say advances in the autonomous vehicle industry will create more jobs than will be lost over time. The road to adoption of these vehicles on a large scale by society will have some potential roadblocks from people impacted negatively in the early stages. The long-term benefits would be a boon to everyone. Hopefully policies will be created for people who will lose their jobs in the short term so the long-term benefits can be reached.

MANAGEABLE EARLY TEST CASES FOR AUTONOMOUS VEHICLES, MORE DIFFICULT CHOICES TO COME

This chapter demonstrates how, particularly during the COVID-19 pandemic, people's trust in automated systems has increased in the US. Nuro has also assisted with the COVID-19 pandemic medical response by offering autonomous delivery vehicles to healthcare workers in California. The world's largest retail store, Walmart, also uses robots to fulfill many tasks to avoid potential coronavirus contamination.

29 Ibid.

While slightly worrying for truck drivers, autonomous vehicle companies have also entered the long-haul freight trucking industry to support the vital supply chain system in the US. The shortage of drivers for the growing demand and efforts by companies to include human drivers in the platoon of vehicles will lessen the job loss in this sector.

There will need to be new regulations, sooner rather than later, for job retraining efforts for taxi drivers, delivery vehicle drivers, and other people at risk of losing their jobs because of the introduction of autonomous vehicles. The US has had little success with these retraining policies in the past. According to an article in *The Atlantic*, efforts at creating federally organized plans have been popular among policymakers even before the Reagan administration. They are unsuccessful because people do not know about them, the classes are disjointed and not relevant to these people's desired work fields, and the job training programs don't force employers to pay workers an adequate wage.[30]

It is unlikely the US will adopt a similar system to the apprenticeship system, which is common and successful in Germany. In this system, workers become apprentices to jobs in different industries. However, the US does have a vast community college system with affordable degree options for people looking to learn new skills to compete in the job market and potentially earn higher wages. Incentive structures such as tax credits for employers who hire workers from retraining programs at decent wages could also be created to assist in this retraining process.

---

30 Lola Fadulu, "Why is the U.S. so Bad at Worker Retraining?," *The Atlantic*, January 4, 2018.

State and local governments, which fund over four trillion dollars for public projects and services every year, will face dire financial decisions for the next several years due to the economic losses from the COVID-19 pandemic. These projects and services include funding for public schools, garbage and recycle truck drivers, parks, museum upkeep, and funding for new infrastructure or repairs for current infrastructure projects.[31]

Estimates by local governments and organizations, such as the US Conference of Mayors and the National League of Cities, project revenue losses of between fifteen and forty-five percent. This would mean reductions of up to $1.75 trillion per year for all of the essential projects and services state and local governments provide. Therefore, states and cities must make tough budgetary choices.[32]

It will be crucial for companies in the autonomous vehicle industry to advocate for funding for infrastructure projects and educational services to assist the people who would lose their jobs in the short term with the adoption of autonomous vehicles by society. I have discussed things such as the importance of things like 5G wireless network connections and "New Infrastructure" projects like smart stoplights. However, basic infrastructure repairs such as repaving and repainting roads are essential for autonomous vehicles to drive safely on public roads. These infrastructure improvements would benefit both conventional and autonomous vehicles to drive more safely.

Ultimately, national, state, and local governments and organizations need to change to allow for a more seamless

---

31 Ted C. Fishman, "America's Next Crisis is Already Here," *The Atlantic*, May 21, 2020.

32 Ibid.

introduction of autonomous vehicles into society while protecting the workforce negatively affected by the introduction of autonomous vehicles. Policies also need to change and adapt over time, as well as the industries involved, for autonomous vehicles to succeed in the US.

CHAPTER 3

THE POTENTIAL POTHOLES AND ROADBLOCKS TO ACCEPTANCE OF AUTONOMOUS VEHICLES IN THE US

THE DIFFICULTIES IN ACHIEVING THE LONG-TERM BENEFITS OF AUTONOMOUS VEHICLES

Amazon sent shockwaves through multiple industries on June 26, 2020 when it announced it had acquired autonomous vehicle startup Zoox. Amazon already has a substantial logistics fleet with their own planes, warehouses, and delivery vehicles.[33]

---

33 Sebastian Blanco, "Amazon Buys Autonomous Tech Company Zoox, and Elon Musk is Amused," *Car and Driver*, June 29, 2020.

Would Amazon then use this purchase to develop autonomous delivery vehicles? Would this lead to Amazon firing its delivery drivers? Would this reduced cost for the drivers lead to cheaper goods for consumers, further affecting both the local storekeepers already hurt by Amazon's dominance in the e-commerce field and the relative ease and cost savings consumers can get from shopping online?

This one purchase of Zoox exemplifies the incredible reach and effect the autonomous vehicle industry can have, even on industries not directly affected by vehicle transportation. Amazon has not discussed its long-term plans for the acquisition of Zoox as far as using the technology to assist in its logistics supply chain is concerned. At present, Amazon has stated it will continue to work with Zoox to establish its passenger ride-hailing fleet.[34]

Zoox will continue with its original business practice from when it was founded in 2014. According to Jeff Wilke, Amazon Worldwide Consumer CEO, "Zoox is working to imagine, invent, and design a world-class autonomous ride-hailing experience." Therefore, the scope of the threat is limited, for now, to people working as taxi drivers and car dealerships with more people using ride-hailing services and not purchasing their own vehicles.[35]

Amazon has experienced expanded e-commerce business with more people shopping online using its e-commerce site instead of shopping in stores. This has greatly increased during the COVID-19 pandemic. Amazon has gained five hundred seventy billion dollars in market capitalization so far in 2020 and is now the third richest company in the world

34 Ibid.

35 Ibid.

at $1.49 trillion, behind only Microsoft MSFT, worth $1.54 trillion, and Apple AAPL, worth $1.61 trillion.[36]

Amazon has the capital to enter virtually any business it wants. It can fund Zoox to continue to develop its autonomous driving system, can wait for regulations to be passed in Congress, and can wait for the technology to mature to start its own ride-hailing fleet. Or it can decide to use that technology for its delivery vehicles now, or several years down the line.

There is still money flooding into the autonomous vehicle industry, as I discussed last chapter, with autonomous goods and food delivery companies receiving over six billion dollars from late 2019 to May 2020. However, investors are becoming more cautious about into which companies they choose to invest money. Autonomous vehicle companies were lucky if they received their series A financing before this economic downturn. Otherwise, they could form partnerships with a major tech company or vehicle manufacturer to survive. The industry itself will survive, but there will be a contraction.

This chapter will discuss the pushback from both organized groups and individuals. Some people fear autonomous vehicles will take their jobs or negatively affect their lives. I will also discuss how there will need to be a change in people's attitude toward vehicle ownership in the US for the long-term benefits to be realized. The perceived strengths the US has in this race, having a history of manufacturing vehicles and a strong driving culture, could actually be a weakness. The lack of this history and driving culture would be a strength for a country like China. Chinese consumers

36 Sergei Klebnikov, "5 5 Big Numbers that Show Amazon's Explosive Growth During the Coronavirus Pandemic," *Forbes*, July 23, 2020.

could more easily accept autonomous vehicles and using a "robotaxi" instead of owning one's own vehicle.

THE LONG ROAD AHEAD FOR AUTONOMOUS VEHICLE SUCCESS IN THE US

Assuming there is overall positive reaction to the initial roll-out of autonomous vehicles, and there is policy assistance for those who would lose their jobs to autonomous vehicles, they could provide incredible long-term benefits to society. They can benefit a large number of people in many different industries. Acceptance of new technologies, particularly those with the potential to disrupt the status quo of many different industries, is essential. The autonomous vehicle industry's push to gain the public's trust and acceptance of autonomous vehicles is discussed throughout this book. There will be accidents along the way, particularly with such a new and possibly dangerous technology. How industry leaders react to the media attention these inevitable accidents will receive will go a long way toward consumer acceptance of the technology.

In a study conducted by Axios of data collected from 2014 to 2018, there were thirty-eight moving vehicle collisions reported in accidents in which at least one of the vehicles was autonomous. Of these accidents, in all but one the human driver was at fault. In the other case, the autonomous vehicle was at fault.[37]

This data could merely reflect there were not as many autonomous vehicles driving on public roads from 2014 to 2018. Also, California is the only state whose DMV required

37 Kia Kolkalitcheva, "People cause most California autonomous vehicle accidents," *Axios*, August 29, 2018.

detailed accident reports for collisions from autonomous vehicle companies. Since the requirements were required by law in California in 2014, there have been a total of 104 vehicle collisions involving at least one vehicle being autonomous.

Another study by Tyson & Mendes shows there were forty-nine total accidents reported in 2018 and one hundred in 2019. Nearly two-thirds of the collisions involved the autonomous vehicle being rear ended by a human driver. This could indicate either a sudden stop by the autonomous vehicle or the human driver expecting the vehicle ahead of it to bend the rules for a "rolling stop" at an intersection, causing the collision. Either way, autonomous vehicle companies need to be aware they will be sharing the road with human-driven vehicles, cyclists, pedestrians, and other micro-mobility options like scooters. Because of this, they need to be programmed to avoid these accidents.[38]

They would need to potentially create a coordinated response to any vehicle accident-related fatalities which might occur. Injuries or deaths will happen hopefully in greatly reduced numbers. However, many people still find accidents involving autonomous vehicles unnerving. Whether autonomous vehicles are held to a higher standard is irrelevant to the public's perception of the situation. A cooperative effort to reassure the media these vehicles are safe will be necessary to regain the public's trust after an accident.

MARKETING CHALLENGES TO AUTONOMOUS VEHICLES

The potential long-term benefits of autonomous vehicles are vast. I will focus on several benefits which directly or

38 Wendy Skillman, "Rare But Instructive Accidents Involving Autonomous Vehicles," *Tyson & Mendes*, January 14, 2020.

indirectly effect millions of people. These benefits will also require changes in how Americans have done things in the past for the impact to be felt on a large scale. These long-term benefits include greater freedom of mobility for blind, disabled, or elderly people, reduced traffic congestion, and the possible reduction of vehicle carbon dioxide emissions.

In one demonstration of autonomous vehicles from an article in *The MIT Technology Review*, the parking lot of Perkins School for the Blind was converted into a testing ground for autonomous vehicles. Optimus Ride, a startup from Cambridge, Massachusetts, drove students and staff on a fixed track in an autonomous vehicle resembling a golf cart. When asked about the experience, principle of the school Dave Power said autonomous vehicles would be "transformative" for people who are blind. He said, "For the first time they will be able to go to school, work, and community activities independently, regardless of distance." He then pointed out there is tremendous enthusiasm for autonomous vehicles in the blind community both at Perkins and nationally.[39]

Organizations for the blind have been working to promote the autonomous vehicle industry from its inception. The National Federation of the Blind (NFB) is the largest organization for blind people in the country. It has advocated for vehicles for the blind since the early 2000s when it organized a Blind Driver Challenge. In this challenge, the NFB encouraged universities and other organizations to create and adopt nonvisual interfaces for vehicles. They have since worked with companies, such as Waymo, to incorporate accessibility features for blind people.[40]

39 Elizabeth Woyke, "The Blind Community Has High Hopes for Self-Driving Cars," *MIT Technology Review*, October 12, 2016.

40 Ibid.

The American Council for the Blind (ACFB) is a national grassroots advocacy group that tracks early autonomous vehicle adopter states' laws concerning autonomous vehicles to ensure they do not prohibit blind people from using them.[41]

While accessibility options may be more of a niche issue for most people, autonomous vehicle industry leaders have lent their support. After introducing his company Waymo, CEO John Krafcik discussed this issue at the 2019 IAA Auto Show in Frankfurt, Germany. He said, "Beyond safety, the freedom that comes with a driver's license isn't even a possibility (for many people)." He continued by saying, "In many developed countries more than twenty percent of the population isn't able to drive due to vision impairment or some other physical disability."[42] Both enthusiastic national and regional organizations and industry leaders have taken my limited vision and millions of other visually impaired, blind, and disabled people's struggles to heart.

I had a conversation with a woman from an organization for the blind who asked to remain anonymous. The opinion is actually fairly mixed with her colleagues in the blind community. She said, "There are people who are in favor of autonomous vehicles and there are people like me who do not want to ride in these vehicles because they are worried about liability concerns." This surprised me, and my only response to this question was what I believe is the truth. Liability is a concern and still needs to be worked out with state or federal regulation, or both, for autonomous vehicles.

This is not a concern limited to the blind community given the incredibly litigious society in the US. I will discuss

41 Ibid.

42 *Waymo*, "2019 IAA Frankfurt Auto Show Remarks by John Krafcik," October 11, 2019, video, 15:41.)

liability and insurance questions in greater detail in my chapter on the policy problems in the US.

I started following the development of the autonomous vehicle industry and became passionate about their development because of my vision difficulties. This was one of the main reasons why I decided to write this book. It was very refreshing for me to see organizations devoted to helping blind people that are actively pushing for legislation at the state and national level to promote autonomous vehicle legislation. It was even more refreshing to learn companies in the autonomous vehicle industry were receptive to these organizations' wishes to make the vehicles more accessible to blind people. This gave me hope that in the future, autonomous vehicles would provide people like me with greater freedom of mobility as well as provide many other benefits to society such as traffic reduction.

SMART INFRASTRUCTURE ROADBLOCKS

The demographic geography of America has evolved to more urban centers. According to data from 2018, the Census Bureau defined eighty percent of Americans as living in urban areas. These urban centers include both large and small cities and the suburban areas immediately outside of these cities.[43] With this rise of urbanization, there has been a corresponding increase in traffic congestion. This traffic congestion has a direct impact on the economy. This issue has become increasingly important for policymakers and the autonomous vehicle industry.

43 Christopher Ingraham, "Americans say there's not much appeal to to big-city living. Why do so many of us live there?," *The Washington Post*, December 18, 2018.

Research about the overall improvement in congestion reduction is still in the early stages. Researchers at the University of Cambridge designed a study which shows fleets of autonomous vehicles working together could reduce traffic congestion by over thirty-five percent. There were some caveats to this study. One of the co-authors of the study, Michael He, stated, "Autonomous vehicles could face a lot of different problems associated with driving in cities, but there needs to be a way for them to work together." Therefore, the penetration of autonomous vehicles on the roads have to be sufficiently high for these vehicles to communicate with each other and reduce traffic.[44]

The different autonomous vehicle companies would need to cooperate to ensure this communication would happen. Another co-author of the study, Nicholas Hyldmar, stated, "If different automotive manufacturers are all developing their own autonomous cars with their own software, those cars all need to communicate with each other effectively." The extent to which autonomous vehicles use penetrates society and the extent to which different companies in the autonomous vehicle industry can work together will be crucial to achieving the thirty-five percent traffic reduction posited by the study.[45]

One of the primary concerns of the technology competition between the US and China is there could be a "One Globe, Two Systems." Without cooperative discussion between the leaders of these countries, there could be a situation in which vehicles from each country cannot communicate with vehicles from the other country. They might also not be able to

44 "Cambridge research into driverless cars finds improved traffic flow," *BBC*, May 21, 2019.

45 Ibid.

communicate with roadside infrastructure designed to assist autonomous vehicles.

Smart infrastructure systems are things like smart stoplights, which can communicate with autonomous or connected vehicles. These smart stoplights would allow for cities to more effectively time stoplight changes depending on the traffic conditions.[46]

China has already been focusing on providing smart infrastructure as part of their push for developing "New Infrastructure" projects. I will describe these systems in further detail in my chapter on Xi Jinping's desire to transform the Chinese economy.

Research institutions and universities are conducting studies on autonomous vehicles and how they can connect to smart infrastructure systems. However, companies in the autonomous vehicle industry in the US are largely focusing on developing the vehicles rather than waiting for the installment of these new infrastructure systems. Other than traffic congestion reduction, another possible benefit would be a reduction of carbon dioxide emissions.

AUTONOMOUS VEHICLES COULD PROVIDE A SOLUTION TO COMBAT CLIMATE CHANGE

The United Nations published data on climate change prevention. In order to avoid the tremendous loss of life and prevent severe economic losses, the world would need to reduce its current greenhouse gas (GHG) emissions by 7.6 percent every year until 2030.[47] Until recently when it was

---

46 Chris Teale, "Cities 'finally waking up' to the benefits of smart streetlights: survey," *Smart Cities DIVE*, May 4, 2020.

47 Fiona Harvey, "UN calls for push to cut greenhouse gas levels to avoid climate chaos," *The Guardian*, November 26, 2019.

replaced by China, the US produced the most GHGs in the world.[48]

Unfortunately, during and after his presidential campaign President Trump promised he would leave the Paris Climate Accords. He referred to climate science as a "hoax" on several occasions.[49] He left the Accords on the first day he could on November 4, 2019.[50]

However, industry has stepped in to develop alternative energy sources, such as solar and wind power, and now employs ten times more people than fossil fuel companies in the US.[51] Depending on the priorities of future presidential administrations and members of Congress, industry will need to continue to take the lead to reduce GHG emissions in the US, including through the autonomous vehicle industry.

Brad Templeton has been a technology and internet pioneer from the early days of the dot-com era. He began advocating for autonomous vehicles back in 2005 because of the incredible benefits they could provide.[52] Not everyone in the autonomous vehicle industry uses electric vehicles. As he said in an interview, "There would be a strong incentive for them to do so." This is because electric vehicles are much easier to maintain, which is important when they will be driving as much as possible as part of a "robotaxi" fleet.

---

48 "Each Country's Share of CO2 Emissions," *Union of Concerned Scientists*, August 12, 2020.

49 Jeremy Schulman, "Every Insane Thing Donald Trump Has Said About Global Warming," *Mother Jones*, December 12, 2018.

50 Lisa Friedman, "Trump Serves Notice to Quit Paris Climate Agreement," *The New York Times*, November 4, 2019.

51 Adam Vaughan, "U.S. green economy has 10 times more jobs than the fossil fuel industry," *NewScientist*, October 15, 2019.

52 Brad Templeton, "Where Robot Cars (Robocars) Can Actually Take Us," *Brad Templeton Home*.

Even with people using "robotaxi" fleets, this does not necessarily mean there will be fewer vehicle miles driven. I interviewed Zifei Yang from the International Council on Clean Transportation (ICCT). She pointed out there might be an incentive for people to ride autonomous vehicles for longer distances because they do not need to pay attention to the road and can work or sleep.

She did describe one tactic used for conventional vehicles to reduce miles driven. There could be a road tax or a fuel tax. For autonomous vehicles, she said, "Maybe if you want to take control of the miles driven, you could charge it by the miles driven or increase the rate."

Some people may still drive for longer distances. However, a study conducted by the US Department of Energy from vehicle data for 2017 shows sixty percent of Americans travel less than six miles one way per trip. People on average drive fewer miles than they did in the past, even if it might take them longer due to the increased traffic.

People in the US have been manufacturing and owning their own vehicles for over one hundred years. The concept of giving up individual ownership of vehicles would represent a drastic change in both US consumer habits and the auto industry in general. People would need to see both the emissions reduction benefits and the traffic reduction benefits with this approach. The consumer attitude could change but it wouldn't happen overnight. There will also be pushback from people in the early stages and lasting potential difficulties the autonomous vehicle industry will also have to overcome.

SPECIAL INTEREST GROUPS CREATE AN UPHILL BATTLE FOR LEGISLATION AND ACCEPTANCE

Back in the 1920s, streetcars were the preferred mode of commuting to work in the United States. Beginning in the 1800s, horse-drawn streetcars that ran on tracks were common.

The horses were replaced by electric streetcars in the 1880s. They were still basically the same and became much more popular as a result. At its peak, there were seventeen thousand miles of streetcar lines in the US and they were a feature in every major city and suburban area in the country. What happened to streetcars, and why do only roughly five percent of American workers commute to work using public transit now?[53]

A popular conspiracy theory speculated GM bought streetcar makers specifically to close them and tear up tracks to make room for automobiles. The truth is streetcar companies went bankrupt and were forced to shut down. There are two main reasons for the financial failings of this previously dominant mode of transportation. The first is vehicles would drive on the track as well as on the roads. This caused traffic congestion, which prevented streetcar from reaching their destinations on time. The second problem was state and city leaders would force streetcar companies to lower their ticket prices. Increased congestion on the roads and the lack of the ability to raise ticket prices killed the streetcar companies and the industry overall in most cities.[54]

Why did the US fail to develop another public transit system to serve as the primary means of worker commutes? A big part of the problem is special interests. This is a problem

---

53 Joseph Stromberg, "The real story behind the demise of America's once-mighty streetcar," *Vox*, May 7, 2016.

54 Ibid.

an authoritarian government, such as China, does not have to deal with. One group in particular, Americans for Prosperity led by Charles and David Koch, fight against new public transit projects at the local and national level. The Koch brothers are two oil billionaires who believe in a libertarian agenda against high taxes and big government. One common victim of this lobbying effort is the public transit systems.[55]

It can be a positive or negative externality of these efforts, depending on your viewpoint, that more people driving on roads also helps their bottom line as oil industry executives. Vehicle manufacturing companies provide either tacit or open support for the fight to block new public transit systems because they see this as beneficial to their vehicle sales. These public transit systems include light-rail trains, bus routes, metro systems and other projects in cities all over the US. These cities include Nashville, Phoenix, Little Rock, southeast Michigan, and central Utah.[56]

The Koch brothers also donate millions of dollars to the campaigns of elected officials at the national and local levels who support their interests. This lobbying effort is critical to achieve their desired policy outcomes. At the local level, they fund and organize grassroots efforts which hire people to go door-to-door to argue against state funding for new public transit projects. Their financial support to conservative politicians during and after their campaigns also grants them leverage in arguing against these transit systems.[57] The money they spend fuels their efforts and leads to states cancelling public transit projects all over the country.

---

55 Hiroko Tabuchi, "How the Koch Brothers are Killing Public Transit Projects Around the Country," *The New York Times*, June 19, 2018.

56 Ibid.

57 Ibid.

While perhaps not as well-funded or influential as the Koch brothers' Americans for Prosperity, there will be people negatively affected by autonomous vehicles. These vehicles might cause truck drivers, taxi drivers, ride-hailing drivers, and postal delivery drivers to lose their jobs. Members of Congress and autonomous vehicle companies must be aware of the economic damages they will cause people in the US. Automation does not kill jobs entirely. There will eventually be more jobs created than lost by autonomous vehicles, but these jobs will not be the same people had before and policymakers should acknowledge such and plan accordingly.

Autonomous vehicles have already been driven on public roads in certain cities in the US to test them. The reaction to these tests has not always been favorable. I talked with Dr. Sven Beiker, founder and managing director of Silicon Valley Mobility. I asked him about the positive and negative feedback he received from people in Silicon Valley related to autonomous vehicles. He said, "Very similar to Arizona, some people in the general public are not happy. They are slitting tires or throwing pebbles at these vehicles. Some people want to just game these vehicles and cut right in front of them." Backlash against these vehicles in a more conservative place like Arizona makes sense if they do not want things to change. Knowing people are acting like this in Silicon Valley, the epicenter of technological innovation in the US, should be slightly troubling for autonomous vehicle companies.

The passenger experience in one of the autonomous shuttles in Silicon Valley is not supported enthusiastically, even by supporters of autonomous vehicles. In my conversation with Dr. Beiker, he talked about taking his eighty-year-old father on a ride in one of these shuttles. His father was unimpressed, saying, "My dad was like oh my god this is so boring. I can walk faster than this thing." Dr. Beiker tried to argue to his father this was the future. Apparently the future was still a few years away from being a fast and reliable transportation option for his father.

Dr. Beiker pointed out these autonomous vehicles are only test vehicles. It remains to be seen what will happen once these vehicles are officially on the market and serving as "robotaxis." How this initial rollout goes and whether people are gradually introduced to the incredible benefits autonomous vehicles can bring to society will be vital for the success of the industry in the US,

HACKERS COULD DERAIL THE AUTONOMOUS VEHICLE INDUSTRY IN THE US

One issue related to autonomous vehicles keeping people up at night would be the possibility these vehicles could be hacked. If these vehicles were hacked, they could inflict significant harm to people. For example, ISIS could hijack an autonomous vehicle and use it to swerve onto a crowded sidewalk in a city. Or a vehicle could be hacked and driven to a remote location housing a criminal intent on murder or kidnapping. All of these worst-case scenarios would be theoretically possible. Autonomous vehicle companies have to make it a priority to ensure the prevention of such incidents.

Conventional vehicles also have computerized components and can be hacked. The most famous instance came in July 2015 when two hackers, Charlie Miller and Chris Valsek, wanted to demonstrate they could remotely take control of a vehicle in a *Wired* news article. They demonstrated this by having a *Wired* reporter drive a Jeep Cherokee on a highway.

They would attempt to hijack the vehicle's Controller Area Network (CAN) bus. The CAN bus is a device which allows the vehicle to communicate with other devices without requiring a host computer.[58]

While the Jeep Cherokee was driving down the highway in traffic, Miller and Valsek accessed the Jeep's CAN bus and disabled the ignition, stopping the vehicle. They then restarted the ignition and allowed the reporter to continue his driving. This demonstrated hackers could take control of the motor functions of a vehicle.[59]

The results of this hack were both embarrassing and costly for Chrysler. They were forced to recall 1.4 million Jeep Cherokee vehicles to install an update so the CAN bus could only be accessed by a third party by plugging it into a computer through a switch under the dashboard.[60]

Uber is developing security systems to prevent hacks to Uber's autonomous driving system. They both returned for another interview about one year later. They described how, while they just cut the ignition and stopped the vehicle, it could have been much worse. Once they took control of the CAN bus, they could perform any of the car's driving functions. For example, they could accelerate, brake, and even turn the steering wheel.[61]

The threat of hacking could derail any of the benefits autonomous vehicles could bring and could cause enormous damage. This issue may involve an autonomous

---

58 Andy Greenberg, "Hackers Remotely Kill a Jeep on the Highway – With Me In It," *Wired*, July 21, 2015.

59 Ibid.

60 Andy Greenberg, "The Jeep Hackers Are Back to Prove Car Hacking Can Get Much Worse," *Wired*, August 1, 2016.

61 Ibid.

vehicle industry leaders, policymakers, and cyber security experts working together to create effective safeguards against fears of hacking. The autonomous vehicle industry should be aware of the very legitimate fear people have related to this issue and address it to the media as much as they discuss safety. After all, these vehicles could potentially be significantly less safe than conventional human-driven vehicles.

The autonomous vehicle industry in the US will have to deal with these issues before it turns its sights to commercializing these vehicles in the US on a large scale. Once autonomous vehicles succeed in the US, autonomous vehicle companies can turn their attention to exporting these vehicles to consumers around the world. Then they need to face the looming competition with Chinese companies. Policy must be created to assist people who will lose their jobs because of autonomous vehicles as soon as possible. If this does not happen, then pressure could cause the industry's development to slow and allow Chinese companies to catch up and take the lead.

A POTENTIAL LOSS IN A RACE THE US WAS BUILT TO WIN

On the surface, the US has many advantages over China in the race to develop the autonomous vehicle. The technology sector in the US is much more developed than in China. The US has been manufacturing vehicles for more than one hundred years, whereas most of the vehicles in China are imported from other countries or are new and unproven.

Finally, the DARPA Grand Challenge in 2004, which was a competition between groups of engineers to drive vehicles autonomously on roads in the Mojave desert, represents the starting point for the autonomous vehicle industry in the US.[62] Meanwhile, the first autonomous vehicle startup in China was Momenta in 2016.[63] Therefore, the US has a twelve-year head start.

This chapter analyzes the safety concerns, which hurt the public's trust in autonomous vehicles. Special interest groups influence the political process as well, making legislation more difficult. Many of the proposed long-term benefits of autonomous vehicles of reducing traffic congestion and carbon dioxide emissions involve shared rides instead of individuals owning their own vehicles. This would represent a dramatic shift in American's consumer habits. The US's long history of producing its own vehicles could actually be a disadvantage with the introduction of autonomous vehicles.

There needs to be a counterweight for special interest groups in favor of autonomous vehicles against those opposed to them in order to accelerate the political process. Companies in the industry also need to expand their educational and marketing efforts as well to convince people of the benefits of shared rides in autonomous vehicles. If these measures are not undertaken, then we can see a similar situation to the one I described at the beginning of last chapter in which the air is clear, a person's dry cleaning would be delivered directly to his or her house, and automated vehicles would get rid of the need for traffic lights and thus substantially increase traffic flow in urban areas. However, this situation would take place in Beijing, instead of Washington, DC.

---

62 Andy Davies, "An Oral History of the DARPA Grand Challenge, the Grueling Robot Race That Launched the Self-Driving Car," *Wired*, August 3, 2017.

63 Rita Liao, "How China's first autonomous driving unicorn Momenta hunts for data," *TechCrunch*, June 13, 2019.

CHAPTER 4

VISION CORRECTION: IDENTIFYING THE BEST WAY FOR AUTONOMOUS VEHICLES TO "SEE" THE WORLD

LIDAR SENSORS: ESSENTIAL FOR AUTONOMOUS DRIVING OR A "FOOL'S ERRAND?"

When Elon Musk talks, people listen. He built Tesla to be one of the largest electric vehicle companies in the world. He also introduced many consumers to semiautonomous driving with Tesla vehicles' level two autopilot feature. Therefore, when he said "LiDAR is a fool's errand. Anyone relying on LiDAR is doomed. Doomed!" at Tesla's recent Autonomy Day, it made headlines.[64]

---

64 Matt Burns, "'Anyone relying on lidar is doomed, Elon Musk says," *TechCrunch*, April 22, 2019.

A less boisterous CEO from a startup company working on autonomous vehicles in China, Dr. Jianxiong Xiao (Professor X) shares a similar opinion. He does not share Musk's strong anti-LiDAR sentiment necessarily. He does argue other companies in the autonomous vehicle industry underestimate the potential of a camera-focused autonomous driving system. He also claims LiDAR sensors are not necessary for vehicles to drive fully autonomously.[65]

LiDAR sensors stands for Light Detection and Ranging sensors. The bulky, honeycomb-shaped object attached to the roof of the vehicle is a LiDAR sensor. LiDAR sensors and cameras are the "eyes" of the autonomous vehicle.

Most companies working on autonomous vehicles in both the US and China disagree, including Waymo, Ford, GM Cruise, Uber, Baidu, Pony.ai, and Didi. They believe LiDAR is an essential part of the sensor stack (LiDAR sensors, cameras, GPS, radar, et cetera) of products for a vehicle to drive autonomously. They argue LiDAR data is equally as crucial as camera imaging data. It is essential for autonomous vehicles to have as many different sensors and cameras as possible for them to accurately perceive the world around them. Why do Musk and Professor X believe LiDAR is unnecessary? Would a vehicle really be able to reach level four or five autonomy (fully autonomous) without it?

LiDAR works much like radar, but instead of sending out radio waves it sends out pulses of infrared light "lasers." These lasers are invisible to the human eye and the sensors measure how long they take to reflect back to the sensor after hitting objects. It does this ten times per second and compiles

65 Tony Peng, "AutoX Wants to Put a Self-driving Car in Your Driveway in Two Years," *Synced*, September 12, 2017.

the results into a point "cloud" that creates a 3D map of the world around the vehicle in real time. The resulting map can identify not only how far away objects are from the car but also what the objects are (another car, a person, a tree, et cetera). The vehicle's computer "brain" can then predict the object's behavior and how the vehicle should drive to avoid the object.[66]

The technological jargon of how the LiDAR sensors work to create the 3D "point cloud" is confusing to the layman. However, LiDAR sensors have recently been installed on popular household cleaning appliances, and the actual operation of what they do is easier to grasp than the technology behind how they do it. I have a friend who is a busy attorney and doesn't have time to clean his beautiful apartment. In addition to dust, often papers and clothes are on the floor.

One day he was going to buy a vacuum that would run by itself. It sounded like a great idea and I was very excited. I was skeptical whether it would work. I said, "I've heard these vacuums constantly get stuck and only clean a small section of your floor." He replied, "No, this one is different. It's more expensive, but it has this LiDAR system to make it follow a specific route and prevents it from getting stuck."

No way, I thought. I had heard of LiDAR sensors before in my research for this book. I took the ad he was holding and glanced at the vacuum he was telling me about. He was right. While more primitive than a vehicle, the technology operates in the same way. The vacuum sends out infrared light "lasers" to map its path. It then travels along this path, avoiding any obstacles along the way. The signals it receives

66 Oliver Cameron, "An Introduction to LIDAR: The Key Self-Driving Car Sensor," *Voyage*, May 9, 2017.

also ensure it does not collide with anything or get stuck in a corner.

LiDAR gives autonomous vehicles "superpowers." It gives them the ability to have a continuous, 360-degree visibility of the world around them. Because the automotive LiDAR system spins at over 600 rpm and emits millions of light pulses per second, the car literally has eyes in the back of its head. LiDAR sensors also allow a vehicle to always know the precise distance of objects from the car, to an accuracy of two centimeters. Radar is then used to determine how fast these objects are moving.[67]

THE DEBATE BEGINS. ARE LIDAR SENSORS NECESSARY?

Aeva, a LiDAR sensor company which provides LiDAR sensors to vehicles, has a partnership with Audi. Audi is also trying to develop autonomous vehicles. The co-founder of Aeva, Soroush Salehian, believes LiDAR sensors are essential for autonomous vehicles to drive safely. He says, "We believe that for a safe stack you must have all the outputs to make the right decision." He then says, "If you're using just a camera sensor, there are so many issues that may blind the system. You need to be able to compliment the different sensor technology weaknesses. Get both outputs and it's up to the carmaker to decide what to do with that information."[68]

What is evident in his statement is a LiDAR sensor is not the only sensor. He also mentions radar and cameras. However, LiDAR is the most important part of the "safe stack."

---

67 Ibid.

68 Liane Yvkoff, "Is Lidar Necessary for Self-Driving Cars? Audi Seems to Think So," *Forbes*, April 17, 2019.

Why do Tesla's Elon Musk and AutoX's Professor X criticize this seemingly miraculous technology? In short, what do they know that the rest of the industry does not? For one thing, LiDAR is a relatively new technology, at least for vehicles. LiDAR sensors were first developed in the 1960s by NASA. They were used in 1971 by the Apollo 15 mission in which astronauts used it to map the surface of the moon.[69] As one of the first glimpses the public had of the surface of the moon, LiDAR's potential seemed limitless.

Before LiDAR sensors were even considered for autonomous vehicles, they provided very useful data for archaeological ventures and agriculture. This was because of their ability to accurately map large scale plots of land.[70] It wasn't until the 2005 DARPA Challenge, where companies and organizations raced fully autonomous vehicles, that the first automobile, Stanley, used LiDAR sensors. The leader who developed the Stanley vehicle went on to lead Google's self-driving car program, details of which are found in my chapter on John Krafcik and Waymo.[71]

This chapter will analyze the debate between a camera-focused autonomous driving system and the system including LiDAR sensors. There is no one perfect answer to this problem of how an autonomous vehicle perceives the world around it. The solution will be to combine the strengths of the different sensors and attempt to minimize all of their weaknesses through merging the data in a process known as "sensor fusion."

---

69 "The History of LIDAR," *Acroname*, January 16, 2020.

70 Ibid.

71 Oliver Cameron, "An Introduction to LIDAR: The Key Self-Driving Car Sensor," *Voyage*, May 9, 2017.

BOTH CAMERAS AND LIDAR SENSORS HAVE LIMITATIONS

Professor X has several complaints about LiDAR sensors, one of which relates to durability concerns. When asked about the durability concerns of LiDAR sensors, Professor X said, "LiDAR doesn't cope well in extreme conditions. Hot and cold temperatures can throw off the sensor calibration, which could disrupt the data produced by the sensors."[72]

Professor X also points out it would be very difficult to have an automotive-grade hardware system with LiDAR last for more than four or five years. This would be assuming it was being used as part of an autonomous "robotaxi" fleet and running almost 24/7. This is because of the huge energy demand of the LiDAR sensors, which leads to wear and tear for the vehicle hardware.[73]

I spoke with Autonomous Vehicle Technical Manager Brian Jee about the issues related to an autonomous vehicle visualizing the world around it. He stated no vehicle will be one hundred percent safe, even if the vehicle has all of the cameras and sensors in the "safety stack." There is a problem with different weather conditions. He revealed potential problems by asking, "What happens if it's raining? We're talking about all this stuff only on sunny, clear days and as soon as there's inclement weather it's all out the window. We don't have a solution for that. It's all band-aids."

Rain or fog can decrease the visibility of cameras and the car becomes roughly five or ten percent less safe. If a bug hits a camera and blocks its view, then the vehicle becomes a certain percentage point less safe. This is why companies like Waymo, Tesla, AutoX, and Baidu test their autonomous

---

72 Mike Brown, "LiDAR is Terrible for Self-Driving Cars, Says AutoX Founder," *Inverse*, April 18, 2017.

73 Ibid.

vehicles in different places with different climates. They want to expose their vehicles to different weather conditions to see how they will react.

Professor X is not the only researcher who shares the concern about LiDAR sensors' durability. In an interview with *The Telegraph* in London, John Rich, the operations chief at Ford Autonomous Vehicles, stated, "We will exhaust and crush a car every four years in this business."[74] This statement has some caveats. The Ford autonomous vehicle will likely be a hybrid car rather than an electric car. Hybrid cars are more complex with more wear and tear, even under normal driving conditions.

Ford, and other autonomous carmakers, will be operating a shared "robotaxi" service, at least at first. This will be used by autonomous vehicle companies as an initial way to make money because the vehicles would be too expensive to be commercially viable to individual consumers. The engines will be running almost 24/7 to continuously pick up and drop off new customers. Even with these caveats, it is still noteworthy that one of the largest automakers in the world is concerned about the longevity of LiDAR sensors.

The image resolution can also be an issue with LiDAR sensors. According to Professor X, "The sensors have a lower resolution than even the cheapest cameras—sixty-four pixels vertically, compared to a VGA camera which has a vertical resolution of four hundred eighty pixels." The classic example is there could be a plastic bag floating in the air and because of the poor image resolution, the vehicle could think the bag

---

74 Olivia Rudgard, "Self-driving cars will only last four years, Ford says," *The Telegraph*, August 25, 2019.

is actually a tire flying toward the vehicle and swerve to avoid the bag. This might cause an accident.[75]

As described by Mr. Jee, currently no clear options exist for inclement weather situations like rain, sleet, or snow. Autonomous vehicle companies have been working on ways to provide a solution to this problem. Each individual camera or sensor has its own specific problems or limitations. However, when they are combined, they offer a potential solution. Multiple cameras or sensors can work together by a process known as "sensor fusion."

"Sensor fusion" is used to detect when a camera or sensor has inaccurate "noise," for example when rain and fog blurring camera visibility. The system then uses filter algorithms so another sensor can make up for the inaccurate "noisy" data from the camera during a rainstorm. The use of this system would require more sensors. This would increase the cost of the vehicle itself. It would also require more computer engineers to program these filters into the car's ADAS "brain." This would increase the R&D and maintenance costs of running an autonomous vehicle company unless another business or financial framework is created by the company.[76]

SENSOR DATA FUSION OFFERS A POTENTIAL SOLUTION, BUT AT A PRICE

The most important criticism of LiDAR sensors is the cost. The cost of the sensors is important because, according to the *2019 Strategy & Digital Auto Report* by Pricewaterhouse-Coopers (PwC), autonomous driving systems will add twelve

75 Mike Brown, "LiDAR is Terrible for Self-Driving Cars, Says AutoX Founder," *Inverse*, April 18, 2017.

76 Jeremy Cohen, "Sensor Fusion," *Towards Data Science*, May 22, 2018.

to twenty-two percent to the price of a vehicle.[77] Most of the increased price is LiDAR sensor systems. A common LiDAR supplier and the inventor of LiDAR sensors for vehicles, Velodyne, set their cost at as high as $8,000 each before recently dropping the price to half that amount.[78]

Different autonomous vehicle companies have different standards for how many LiDAR sensor "pucks" are necessary for each vehicle. Waymo, for example, uses three custom-built LiDAR sensors in every vehicle in its new Fifth-Generation Jaguar I-Pace autonomous electric SUV. One sensor is for longer ranges, which Waymo claims can clearly see three hundred meters away as opposed to the maximum range of Velodyn's at two hundred meters. They each also include sensors for both short- and medium-range visibility.[79]

PwC's 2019 Digital Auto Report states suppliers and OEMs, or original equipment manufacturers (organizations which manufacture devices from component parts bought from other organizations), would have to cut technology costs by sixty-five to seventy-five percent by 2030 for autonomous vehicles to be profitable.[80]

I spoke to a business consultant and friend who specializes in advising new technology companies, including autonomous vehicle companies, and asked his name and company

---

77 Helko Weber, Jorg Krings, Jonas Seyfferth, Hartmut Guthner, Jorn Neuhausen, et al., "*The* 2019 Strategy& Digital Auto Report," *Price-waterhouse* Cooper, accessed February 23, 2020.

78 Chris Davies, "A key part of many autonomous cars just got a huge pay cut," *Slash* Gear, January 2, 2018.

79 Alex Davies, "Waymo's Self-Driving Jaguar Arrives With New, Homegrown Tech," *Wired*, March 4, 2020.

80 Helko Weber, Jorg Krings, Jonas Seyfferth, Hartmut Guthner, Jorn Neuhausen, et al., "*The* 2019 Strategy& Digital Auto Report," *Price-waterhouse* Cooper, accessed February 23, 2020.

remain anonymous. I asked him about the need for a drastic reduction in the technology cost of autonomous vehicles stated in the PwC's report. He began by talking about the automotive industry from the perspective of OEMs. He said, "For the OEMs, it's like a ticket to the future (for potentially significant profits). Long term, they remain very confident about when they check this ticket, but their primary focus is still on the conventional vehicles because that's how they are making money." Autonomous vehicles need to have mature technology and a mature business strategy before they are produced on a large scale and become profitable.

Why does the added cost of LiDAR sensors make Musk and Professor X hesitant to join the rest of the companies in the industry in adding LiDAR sensors to their autonomous driving "safety stack?" For Elon Musk, who recently sold his one millionth electric vehicle at Tesla, he would like to begin producing large numbers of autonomous Tesla vehicles as soon as possible. Even if Tesla made its own LiDAR sensors like Waymo does, it would be hard to mass produce five hundred thousand Tesla vehicles with such a technically complex sensor system. It would also be difficult, if not impossible at this time, to price the vehicles so an individual consumer would be able to afford them.

Meanwhile, Professor X's hesitation to include LiDAR sensors at AutoX is based, at least in part, on his personal background. Because he grew up in a poor family that never owned a car, he claims "autonomous driving should not be a luxury" and wants to make the option of driving in an autonomous vehicle an option for everyone.[81]

---

81 Yifan Yu, "Professor X readies self-drive cars for China's busy streets," *Nikkei Asian Review*, August 23, 2019.

It's up for debate whether these statements are just for publicity or from a sense of genuine altruism. Professor X has a PhD from MIT and has specialized training in camera vision tactics. These tactics would allow cameras at different angles to create 3D images of the world around the vehicle. Therefore, this statement could be a combination of altruism and speaking from a position of technical expertise.[82]

At Tesla's Autonomy Day, Andrej Karparthy, senior director of AI at Tesla, described how cameras provide the data necessary for the vehicle to drive autonomously. Karparthy claims the world is built for visual recognition. According to Karparthy, "In that sense, LiDAR is really a shortcut." He continued on to say, "It sidesteps the fundamental problems, the important problem of visual recognition, that is necessary for autonomy. It gives a false sense of progress and is ultimately a crutch."[83] Tesla believes the higher resolution images received by the cameras can provide better data for object recognition and then the automated driving system "brain" can more easily recognize and avoid obstacles.

As a test of the legitimacy of this approach, Professor X bought fifty-dollar cameras at Best Buy and added them to an AutoX vehicle equipped with his "computer learning" and autonomous driving systems. "It could not be cheaper than that," Professor X said. In the video of the test, the car handled a number of different driving tasks with ease. While this was just a short demonstration, it did demonstrate a

---

82 Ibid.

83 Matt Burns, "Anyone relying on lidar is doomed, Elon Musk says," TechCrunch, April 22, 2019.

vehicle can drive autonomously even when it only uses cheap cameras to provide it with visual data.[84]

Professor X and Elon Musk do not just use cameras in their vehicles. Even though they represent outliers because they do not use LiDAR sensors, they use ultrasonic sensors which are sensors with limited range. They detect static vehicles for things like parking. Their vehicles also have GPS so the vehicle knows where it is, and odometers and wheel sensors to measure the speed it is travelling by measuring the displacement of the wheels.[85] The vehicles also have radar, which can detect where objects are in relation to the vehicle and determine their velocity. Because of the limited image resolution of radar, it cannot properly identify the object.[86]

Recently there have been two significant developments in relation to LiDAR sensors. The first is Bosch, the popular Tier-1 parts supplier for vehicles, that announced in January 2020 at the Consumer Electronics Show in Las Vegas, Nevada it will be producing LiDAR sensors for autonomous vehicle.[87]

This is significant because Bosch aims to lower the cost of this technology by exploiting economies of scale. "By filling the sensor gap, Bosch is making automated driving a viable possibility in the first place," said Harold Kroger, member of Bosch's management board. It is still too early to know if this will be the case. It could potentially solve the worries about the price of LiDAR sensors and allow for upscaling the production of this technology because Bosch is a trusted

---

84 Jack Stewart, "AutoX Slaps $50 Webcams on a Car to Make it Drive Itself," *Wired*, March 22, 2020.

85 Jeremy Cohen, "Sensor Fusion," *Towards Data Science*, May 22, 2018.

86 Ibid.

87 "Bosch Unveils Lidar Sensor for Autonomous Driving," *GIM International*, January 9, 2020.

Tier-1 supplier of other vehicle components, like radar and cameras.[88]

Another new development of note is the Cheetah LiDAR sensor system designed by Innovusion, Inc. This LiDAR system uses a unique rotating polygon approach which is combined with proprietary detector electronics, advanced optics, and sophisticated software algorithms. While how it works may be confusing to non-technophiles, the Cheetah LiDAR system has a detection range of two hundred meters and can detect objects as far as two hundred eighty meters. The sophisticated rotating polygon framework allows for image-quality resolution of three hundred vertical pixels.[89]

The innovative design also allows the Cheetah LiDAR system to run at under forty Watts, which is claimed to be the most energy efficient of any high-quality LiDAR system. The price of thirty-five thousand dollars for low quantities could scare people, but Innovusion claims with this system used as the primary sensor in the "safety stack, there would only be the need for one LiDAR sensor.[90]

Assuming the vehicle is a new fifth generation Waymo autonomous vehicle, equipped with all of the different sensors, how exactly does the "sensor fusion" work to ensure the optimal way for the vehicle to perceive its surroundings? Each sensor has different advantages and disadvantages. Cameras are the best tools to detect roads, read signs, or recognize another vehicle or pedestrian. LiDAR sensors are better at accurately estimating the position of the vehicle in

88 Ibid.

89 "innovusion Launches Image-Grade LiDAR System 'Cheetah'," *The Economic Times*, June 17, 2019.

90 Ibid.

relation to other objects. Radar is used to accurately estimate the speed of the different objects it detects.[91]

To merge the data with "sensor fusion," people use an algorithm called a Kalman filter. This is one of the most popular algorithms for data fusion and is used by cell phones and satellites for navigation and tracking. It was most famously used in the Apollo 11 mission to send the crew to the moon and bring them back.[92]

How the Kalman filter works specifically can get very technical and involve complex mathematical algorithms. A Kalman filter can be used for data fusion (data from two different sensors at once) to measure the state of a system. This state can be dynamic (evolving with time), in the present (filtering), the past (smoothing), or the future (predictive).[93]

For example, an autonomous vehicle could receive data from cameras indicating a pedestrian jaywalking crossing the street is travelling at eight miles per hour and is in the middle of the road. However, radar could say the pedestrian is crossing the street at only five miles per hour. By performing a fusion of data from different sensors using the Kalman filter, the "noise" generated by either filter is reduced.

This allows the vehicle to more accurately judge the speed in which the pedestrian is crossing the road. This can be done to more accurately measure the distance of an object from the vehicle as well if sensors are merged with the LiDAR and radar. Different sensors can produce a more accurate perception of the world around the vehicle and allow it to drive more safely.

---

91 Jeremy Cohen, "Sensor Fusion," *Towards Data Science,* May 22, 2018.

92 Ibid.

93 Ibid.

The specific mechanism for merging these sensors can be incredibly complex. The sensor data itself can be vastly different between different sensors. There is the image data received by cameras and the 3D "point cloud" generated by LiDAR sensors. The camera data would need to be scaled down to the image resolution of the LiDAR data to be compatible, and then have a scaling algorithm to increase the image resolution of the objects. This would also all need to take place in real time, or as quickly as possible. Autonomous vehicle companies are working hard to perfect the vehicle's perception of the world around it and developing these "sensor fusion" algorithms represents the best way to make this happen.[94]

LOOKING AT THE ROAD AHEAD

Ultimately, no sensor can work alone for an autonomous vehicle to drive safely. I asked a business consultant who advises new technology clients, including autonomous vehicle companies, whether cameras could replace LiDAR sensors for autonomous vehicles. He responded immediately, saying, "I am very skeptical about the Tesla technological focus on cameras and I know a lot of the people I've talked to in the industry are very skeptical about that technology as well." He went on to say, "The cameras are constrained by a lot of weather conditions…For one of my studies I was looking into the camera route and the cameras just can't take you to level five (fully autonomous) because you need a backup and you need a reserve systems for full security...It's irresponsible tech to focus only on the camera side."

---

94 Ibid.

The criticism that the cameras do not do well in many weather conditions was mentioned earlier by Soroush Salehian of Aeva. It is a common criticism from vehicle manufacturers. The key takeaway from this assessment is, while Professor X can have a short demo using cheap cameras, a vehicle relying primarily on cameras would not be able to drive autonomously at level four or five unless it included LiDAR sensors and the full "safety stack" of sensors.

The rate of new technology advancements for autonomous vehicles is impressive. After all, LiDAR sensors have only been used on vehicles for fifteen years. Researchers will continue to develop new and cheaper technology to make perception of the world around the vehicle better. However, removing sensors from the "safety stack" to decrease the price is not the answer for autonomous vehicle companies. The answer to reducing costs while maintaining the safety of the vehicles will be in creating new business and financial models for them.

There appears to be no easy solution to this problem. Companies must focus on combining sensor data in "sensor fusion" to take advantage of the strengths of all the different sensors and minimize their weaknesses. Joint financing, having third party companies run tests of the vehicle's autonomous driving "brain" to reduce R&D costs, and using autonomous vehicles for shared "robotaxi" fleets are ways to reduce the costs of these vehicles. This book explores several of these new business models. How they develop will be critical for the success of autonomous vehicles in both the US and China.

CHAPTER 5

DISSECTING THE CENTRAL NERVOUS SYSTEM OF THE AUTONOMOUS VEHICLE

THE DEVELOPMENT OF ARTIFICIAL INTELLIGENCE AND AUTONOMY BEFORE AUTONOMOUS VEHICLES

In the 2019 remake of the horror film *Child's Play*, there is a scene in which a woman had her first experience driving an autonomous vehicle. As she drives, a young boy runs to the street corner and yells for her to stop the car and get out, but she can't hear him. She approaches her destination: a restaurant in a shopping center. She is thrilled by the experience of driving the car without having to control it herself.

Her excitement turns to terror after the car pulls over in front of the restaurant. The car stops and begins to reverse, gains speed, spins around, and speeds to a deserted shopping center. The car accelerates, zooming through the shopping center, and slams on the brakes in front of a store.

Directly in front of the car stands a doll with straight red hair, glowing red eyes, and a maniacal grin. With a twitch of the doll's finger, the car reverses and spins around. The doll then disables the airbag and removes the woman's seat belt. The car gains speed and rams into another vehicle. The car then tells the woman, "You have arrived at your destination." Then it is replaced by the doll's voice, who says, "I see you…"[95]

This scene portrays the fear of many people in the US that the machine driving autonomous vehicles is beyond our power to control and is therefore dangerous. Autonomous vehicles are not just some futuristic machine from sci-fi or horror movies. Autonomous vehicle companies may differ on which cameras or sensors they use, but the technology they use for the autonomous driving system is basically the same.

There is human control in every aspect of the vehicle development, production, and testing. Humans are involved in everything from designing the vehicle, coding the automated driving system, to testing the vehicles on both private test tracks, driving simulations, and public roads. Even after the vehicles are produced and deployed, there will be large tele-monitoring centers for each company to monitor its vehicle fleet. This system is not perfect, but it is incorrect to say there is no human control over autonomous vehicles.

The system is also not even very new. Allen Turing used rudimentary machine learning technology to crack Nazi codes during World War II. During World War II, a single computer took up an entire room.[96] Computing power has

---

95 *Serieslove*, "Child's Play (2019) – Chucky kills Doreen," October 13, 2019, video, 2:46.

96 Rockwell Anyoha, "The History of Artificial Intelligence, *Harvard University: The Graduate School of Arts and Sciences*, August 28, 2017.

increased exponentially since then. However, is this increase in computing power enough to replicate the incredibly complex task of driving a vehicle? A dissection of the computer "central nervous system" driving the vehicle must be undertaken to discern whether it can drive as safely, or safer, than a human.

When referring to autonomous systems in general, some people complain they cost people jobs. That might be true for jobs in the manufacturing industry for people who previously worked on automobile and other manufacturing jobs. Automation makes it possible to mass produce millions of vehicles or other products every year around the world. Jobs are not necessarily lost entirely with this massive increase in efficiency, but they certainly change.

For example, new jobs created after an automated manufacturing system is introduced may include engineering jobs to keep the machines running smoothly. Or there could be jobs for designing new makes or models of vehicles or other manufactured items on the creative side. Jobs requiring complex decision making or consumer-facing jobs involving contact with customers might also need a human because these positions are not well-suited for automated systems.

Chris Dues explained this process in an interview. Mr. Dues has worked in the software industry for over ten years, with a major focus on recruitment automation. The majority of his experiences have been building and implementing high volume hiring systems for some of the largest corporations in the world. These systems use machine learning (ML) and natural language processing (NLP) to create and/or update candidate profiles in a database known as Applicant Tracking Systems for their respective client companies. These systems are invaluable to the companies because it would be practically impossible for a hiring manager to carefully analyze thousands of job applications for each job.

Mr. Dues explained these types of services are not perfect because it sometimes has trouble recognizing more complex statements about a person's work history. He said, "Even if it retains seventy or eighty percent accuracy in terms of extracting job qualifiers, then it's doing a great job." The pool of possible candidates then moves to the hiring manager(s) of his client's companies and people are invited for interviews to find the right person for the opening.

In the past year, Mr. Dues has changed his focus on how to better engage candidates through automation. He currently works for Herefish, Inc., which is an automated candidate engagement platform. He is currently working seventy hours per week during the COVID-19 pandemic to get automation in the hands of his clients.

Herefish is a platform which allows companies to quickly market open job opportunities to candidates. It ensures the hiring process runs smoothly and efficiently for the candidates. He stated, "There are over thirty million people out of work in the United States, and automation is the key tool we're going to use to get them back to work." By allowing automation to focus on the candidate experience and ensuring candidates are kept in the loop of new jobs, application status, and follow up activities, autonomy eliminates the human error that inevitably causes delays in the hiring process. This will allow Herefish to quickly put people back to work.

He said when the economy starts to recover "we can still have the automation layer, but it allows us now to start building a more specialized work force...of people thinking outside the box and handling complex situations."

Automation creates a win-win situation. Companies can achieve basic functions much more efficiently using automation for basic tasks, but they would still need to hire people for more complex work requiring creativity to fulfill more specific tasks.

The autonomous driving system "brain" of autonomous vehicles is relatively new. The first Defense Advanced Research Projects Agency (DARPA) Grand Challenge featured fifteen groups of engineers who drove autonomous vehicles in the Mojave Desert on March 13, 2004. The result of this test were engineers instructing autonomous vehicles to run before they learned to walk. There were SUVs, dune buggies, a monster truck, and even a motorcycle. The result was vehicles crashing into each other, a broken fence near the road, and vehicles dragging barbed wire into the desert sand. In short, the scene resembled more of a vehicle scrapyard than a race.[97]

It may not have been a technological success at the time, but it demonstrated the possibilities of autonomy and inspired hope for the future. Only one year later, at the second DARPA Grand Challenge, twenty-three of the twenty-four teams drove further than the best vehicle from the first challenge (7.32 miles). Five teams completed the entire track of one hundred thirty-two miles.[98]

Developing the basic technology for autonomy in general represents a very complex system, even for trained computer engineers. The computer codes and algorithms embedded

97 Alex Davies, "An Oral History of the Darpa Grand Challenge, the Grueling Robot Race That Launched the Self-Driving Car," *Wired*, August 3, 2017.

98 Steve Russell, "DARPA Grand Challenge Winner: Stanley the Robot," *Popular Mechanics*, January 9, 2006.

in the vehicle's automated driving system are able to both perceive the world around the vehicle and react to things like traffic and pedestrians. The specific mechanisms which make this happen take time and experience to improve the vehicle's functioning and safety.

The closest analogy for how the autonomous vehicle's driving system works and improves is the human brain and central nervous system. There are four stages in this autonomous driving system which involve perception of the world around the vehicle, applying computer neural networks, and deep learning. How the vehicle knows its relative position in the world (its location, speed, et cetera), deciding on the safest plan of action to move closer to the intended destination and, performing driving functions (stopping, accelerating, turning, et cetera) to execute the previous decided plan are all performed within this system.[99]

All of these stages need to happen at the same time, or as fast as possible, for the vehicle to drive safely. I will describe each stage individually so it is more easily understood.

HOW AN AUTONOMOUS VEHICLE PERCEIVES THE WORLD

Before an automated system can create the "win-win" situation described by Chris Dues, it needs a basic coding structure. Algorithms represent the basic building blocks of all of the efficiency boosting power of autonomous systems and the system driving autonomous vehicles. Algorithms are mathematical formulas informing a computer about how to solve problems using a given set of data.[100]

99 Elizabeth Rivelli, "How Do Self-Driving Cars Work and What Problems Remain?," *The Simple Dollar*, June 30, 2020.

100 Stephen F. Deangelts, "Artificial Intelligence: How Algorithms Make Systems Smart," *Wired*, September, 2014.

This may seem like a nerdy collection of numbers and commands to a non-technophile. However, the systems these algorithms create produce the massive efficiency boosting AI and machine learning "brain" of automated systems. Think of them, when operating with other algorithms, as neural pathways sending information to the computer "brain" and returning with information to act at incredibly high speeds.

As AI research progressed, researchers sought to mimic human decision making to carry out tasks in increasingly more human ways. The machines learn from each successful attempt and get better at these processes over time. Machine learning is a current application of AI. We give machines access to large quantities of data and let them learn through repetition of the same task or tasks thousands or millions of times.[101]

Mr. Dues explained machine learning by saying, "Machine learning is the construction of algorithms that are constructed by people or at least monitored by people, which can make predictions based on certain sets of data." For autonomous vehicles, computer engineers write many core algorithms related to the primary functions of the vehicle to stop, accelerate, change lanes, or turn.

These algorithms are able to process huge amounts of data from the cameras and other sensors when the car drives or the system is run through different computer simulations. Autonomous vehicles have several different types of algorithms. These algorithms constantly render the surrounding environment and predict the changes in this environment

---

101 Karen Hao, "What is Machine Learning," *MIT Technology Review*, November 17, 2018.

to drive safely. Together they focus on four tasks: detecting an object, identifying the object, object localization (how far away the object is from the vehicle), and predicting the object's movement.[102]

An autonomous vehicle must be taught about what it may see and encounter before it ever drives on roads. This process is called "supervised training." According to Brian Jee, "This is an incredibly laborious process and even subject to human error." He explained autonomous vehicle companies' machine learning teams send camera and LiDAR sensor data to companies called data annotation services to manually identify and note objects in single frames of camera or LiDAR images. These companies operate in places where labor costs are low in places like India, the Philippines, and Kenya. Millions of annotated images are then put back into machine learning models to improve algorithmic performance in identifying objects previously noted through human labor.

People work in big factory complexes and go through the camera or LiDAR data. They make a box around all of the objects in the frame of the photo. These objects could include things like cars, traffic cones, a green light, or yellow arrow on a stoplight.

The workers then identify the objects and click on a dropdown menu to describe the "attribute(s)" of that object. The attribute would be what the object does or signifies. An example would be how a mailbox would just be a stationary object on the sidewalk. However, a traffic cone is placed on the road itself and signifies there is an accident or road

---

102 Victor Haydin, "How Machine Learning Algorithms Make Self-Driving Cars a Reality," *intellias*, October 11, 2018.

construction ahead. The vehicle would then need to either change lanes, drive more slowly, or both.[103]

Mr. Jee noted human perception inaccuracy may occur because whatever is outside of the object in the box (the air, road, grass, et cetera) is just treated as blank space, or for example, a bicycle was mislabeled as a motorcycle. Great effort is taken to draw boxes as close to the objects of interest in the images down to the pixel level of resolution and to verify labels.

Despite these efforts, Chevy Cruise's autonomous driving system confused a large delivery truck with its back door wide open on a narrow San Francisco road for a tunnel. The car then attempted to drive into it because no one had classified the object as a truck with an open door. A significant challenge is to anticipate and collect millions of images of everything a car could ever encounter on the road, even delivery trucks with open doors.

The companies operating the factories where all of the people identify objects and list their attributes claim their companies have a ninety-five percent safety rate for properly identifying objects and listing their attributes. Up to five percent inaccuracy is often acceptable in quality control agreements between clients and data annotation firms. That five percent may also include human error such as incorrectly labeling an object as something it is not. However, it is the extra fiver percent that is not properly identified or has not had all of its attributes listed which can cause these bizarre scenarios to occur.

---

103 "Machine Learning Algorithms in Self-Driving Cars," *DexLab*, March 27, 2020.

The deep learning system, responsible for the vehicle's perception of the world around it, is most analogous to the cerebral cortex in the human brain. The cerebral cortex is what most strongly distinguishes humans from other animals. It is responsible for high-level thinking, problem solving, language, planning, vision, and pattern recognition.[104] For an autonomous vehicle, data is collected from LiDAR sensors, radar, ultrasonic, and cameras mounted on the vehicle.

These cameras and sensors are the "eyes" of the vehicle. This data is processed through computer code algorithms known as "neural networks." Each neural network controls only one task.[105] Millions of neural networks are in the deep learning system, just like over seven trillion nerves are in the human body.[106]

According to Brian Jee, "Neural networks are trying to find patterns in the fastest time possible. Elementary linear algebra is performed on the sensor data very quickly, in a matter of milliseconds, to find patterns in sensor data." All of the objects with their list of attributes are stored in the autonomous driving system's hard drive. Neural networks must compare the data of what it "sees" from the cameras or LiDAR sensors to the data patterns already stored in the system as fast as possible. For example, neural networks compare a green round light on a stoplight to the millions of other similar green round lights it was trained with. They match that pattern and the attribute that this green light

---

104 "Cerebral Cortex," *Brain Made Simple*, September 26, 2019.

105 Katie Burke, "How Do Self-Driving Cars Make Decisions?," *NVIDIA Blog*, May 7, 2019.

106 NorthEast Spine and Sports Medicine, "Important Nerves in the Body and What They Do," *Spine and Sports Medicine Blog*, May 8, 2020.

means “go.” Therefore, the vehicle should continue to drive through the intersection.

This system needs to be as mathematically simple as possible because, as Mr. Jee described to me, “Meanwhile, you’re going thirty-five miles per hour and the computer is going full blast trying to perform this computation ASAP.” With more miles driven autonomously, and more objects added with accurate descriptions of their attributes, the deep learning system can make this pattern recognition process happen faster. This increase in speed allows the vehicle to drive more safely.

Why have there been so many delays in producing autonomous vehicles if companies have had at least a deep learning prototype for perception on their vehicles for ten years, at least in the case of Waymo? Autonomous driving would not be as complicated if everyone followed the rules, lines on the roads were clearly painted, and there was no traffic congestion. This is not the case because cars swerve into lanes, run red lights, and lines are not always clearly painted. This makes even human driving more difficult.

With greater urbanization, traffic congestion has also increased in many cities all over the world. This cuts down the time able to stop or move to the side to avoid a collision with another car to mere fractions of a second. Jaywalking by pedestrians presents a constant problem as well, particularly in cities. Vehicles must pay attention to objects on the sidewalks as well as the road.

These types of irrational behavior are called “edge cases.” Coding all of these edge cases into the automated driving system involves an estimated one billion lines of code to create the algorithms for the neural networks for a fully autonomous vehicle. To put this into perspective, NASA only needed one hundred forty-five thousand lines of code for the Apollo 11 Spaceship that travelled to the moon. Therefore, autonomous vehicles would need roughly one thousand times more lines of code than a spaceship which travelled to the moon and back.[107]

Mr. Jee described the problem of coding edge cases into the vehicle's system, saying, "As a human driver if I'm coming up to an intersection and there's a tree down in the middle of the road, then there's a police officer standing there, waving people through the intersection." He stated there is no way to code that into the vehicle right now, but there will be context and behavioral prediction.

In this case, the context would be the police officer waving people through to avoid the tree. The behavioral prediction would be to slow down and only move when the officer motions for the vehicle to move. This becomes very complicated to code into the system. He mentioned another example in which a young boy is walking on the sidewalk playing with a ball. A human driver knows they need to slow down because the ball could bounce onto the road and the boy could run in front of the car to chase it. However, that would require both context and predictive behavior.

At this point, there would need to be an alert from the car to a tele-monitoring office. Then someone from the office could either activate an emergency protocol for the vehicle with the required predictive behavior or take control of the car to avoid a collision. In order for a signal to be transmitted and for the tele-monitor to react, there would need to be a high-speed wireless connection. This is one of the reasons

---

107 Tristan Shale-Hester, "Driverless cars will require one billion lines of code, says JLR," *Auto* Express, April 16, 2019.

why Chinese companies like Huawei and ZTE are investing billions of dollars in 5G wireless connectivity.[108]

One study of the lack of context and predictive behavior coded into the autonomous driving system attempted to address the issue described by Mr. Jee. According to the study, treating every vehicle like an obstacle which must be avoided at all costs and every human driver as the same person presents challenges. This has led to bottlenecking and complaints from human drivers in places like Arizona and Beijing. Pilot autonomous vehicles are *too* polite at places like four-way stop signs. This holds up the traffic.

A study conducted by researchers at the MIT Computer Science and Artificial Intelligence Laboratory (CSAIL) seeks to teach autonomous vehicles to act more like human drivers. The research team wants to accomplish this task through incorporating tools from social psychology to better understand how selfish or altruistic a driver is. Specifically, they used something called social value orientation (SVO), which is a character spectrum ranging from selfish to altruistic, or cooperative. The system then estimates drivers' SVOs to create real time traffic trajectories for autonomous vehicles.[109]

The theory of incorporating driver SVO estimates into the autonomous vehicle driving system was tested on two case studies. For an unprotected left turn, the data analyzed by footage from actual drivers showed drivers should be more hesitant to turn unless there is no oncoming traffic. For merging onto a road while parked, the data suggested a more selfish, aggressive approach. "Creating more human-like

---

108 Alex Davies, "The War to Remotely Control Self-Driving Cars Heats Up," *Wired*, March 26, 2019.

109 Larry Hardesty, "Making driverless cars change lanes more like human drivers do," *MIT News*, May 22, 2018.

behavior in autonomous vehicles is fundamental for the safety of passengers and surrounding vehicle," says graduate student Wilko Schwartzing, the lead author of the study.[110]

To recap, millions of objects are detected and identified with the attributes for each item. These files are then stored in the autonomous vehicle's computer hard drive. As the vehicle drives, data from the cameras and LiDAR sensor's, or the "eyes" of the vehicle, are sent to the computer "cerebral cortex." In the "cerebral cortex," neural networks compare this visual data to the files stored in the hard drive, along with all of the attributes for the objects. The vehicle can then perceive the world and identify the attributes of the objects in a system called a deep learning neural network. This whole process is performed continuously and must happen as fast as possible for the vehicle to drive safely.

There are three other stages in the autonomous driving system. These stages take place at the same time, or as close to the same time as possible. These three steps relate to how the vehicle knows about itself (its location and speed), how the vehicle plans its actions based on the information it receives from the deep learning neural network, and how the vehicle acts on the information it gets from the path planning system.

THE AUTONOMOUS VEHICLE DISCOVERS WHERE IT IS AND WHAT TO DO NEXT

Autonomous vehicles have information from their "eyes" and the neural networks process that information into a perception of the world in the deep learning system. However, several other sensors on the vehicle allow it to better understand

---

110 Ibid.

itself as well. This step is important because the vehicle needs to know as much information about where it is and how fast it is going to know when to perform certain driving functions. These functions could include when to brake or change lanes to avoid an accident.

Autonomous vehicles have a GPS in order to determine in general where they are in the world. Depending on the GPS signal and cloud conditions, the GPS can determine where the vehicles are within one meter. Autonomous vehicles also have an Inertial Measurement Unit (IMU) which tells it what direction it's facing. This allows the vehicle to determine whether it is approaching an object or moving away from it. Gyroscopes and the accelerometer measure the angle, or incline and decline, of the road the vehicle is on and sensors on the wheels tell the vehicle about its velocity.[111]

All of these additional sensors are important because whether a vehicle is on a hill and how fast it is going provides information for when to brake or speed up. Continuing with the analogy of the brain and central nervous system, this would be the posterior parietal cortex (PPC) of the brain. The PPC is responsible for planning movements and spatial awareness.[112]

For an example, the GPS tells the vehicle it is on Main Street in the left lane while the IMU tells the vehicle it is facing the downtown part of the city. The gyroscopes and accelerometer show the vehicle is climbing a slight hill and the wheel speed sensors and accelerometer show it is moving

111 Mike Horton, "IMU Technology Forms the Brains of the Autonomous Vehicle," *5G Technology World*, February 14, 2019.

112 Matt Wood, "Area of brain associated with spatial awareness and planning action also plays crucial role in decision making," *University of Chicago Medicine*, July 10, 2019.

at thirty miles per hour. Brian Jee summarized this whole process by saying, "You kind of figure out, 'okay, I know where I'm going, I know how I'm moving, I think I know how to get to the next desired point.'"

At this stage, the autonomous vehicle has perceived the world around it through the path planning. It knows where it is, its speed, and the incline of the road through the different sensors I just described, and it knows where its final destination is. Now it just needs to act on all of the information to try to get there.

To complete the central nervous system of the vehicle, the final related steps are known as the path planning level and the controls level. In the path planning level, path planning algorithms receive sensor data from LiDAR sensors and cameras and generate a plan for the vehicle's driving actuators to accelerate, decelerate, brake, or change lanes. In the controls level, the vehicle responds to the information it receives from the path planning algorithms. It then performs all of the necessary driving functions.[113]

In the autonomous vehicle's central computer, effective path planning algorithms are what makes autonomous driving feasible, safe, and fast. Predicting the behavior of traffic agents (other cars, pedestrians, cyclists, et cetera) around the autonomous vehicle is one of the most difficult challenges to reaching full level five autonomy. The path planning stage means deciding what autonomous vehicles will do in the future. Models for motion prediction and planning are mostly built on a rules-based system. However, the future is uncertain and not all of the other traffic agents around

---

113 Chris Angelini, "Security on the road: Locking down tomorrow's connected vehicles," *VentureBeat*, September 13, 2019.

the autonomous vehicle follow the rules. Pedestrians could jaywalk, other cars could cut the vehicle off, or a vehicle could drive through an intersection without stopping or run a red light. As the number of traffic agents increases, in urban areas for example, the number of potential difficulties increases proportionally.[114]

A supervised learning approach, in which coded path planning algorithms are created for every traffic agent and their predictive behavior, could resolve this concern. However, this would require the collection of a lot of data to create path planning algorithms for rare and unexpected "edge case" scenarios. After this data is collected and stored in the central computer's hard drive, inputs and outputs need to be created for the LiDAR sensors and camera data for a path planning model. Sensor data of the world around the vehicle, with all of the traffic actors, is sent to the path planning algorithm model through the system's input. The path planning algorithms in the model decide what the vehicle should do to drive safely and then send this information through the system's output to the controls level.[115]

The process of sending the data signals to the vehicle's actuators (the steering wheel, gear shift selector, accelerator, and brake pads) happens through several computers or computing systems in the controls level. The perception data from the cameras, LiDAR sensors, radar, and so on is sent to a central computer through various cables and in-vehicle networks, such as automotive ethernet cables, CAN bus (Controller Area Network), or serial cables. These cables are

---

114 Luca Bergamini, Vladimir Iglovikov, Filip Hlasek, and Peter Ondruska, "Prediction Model for Autonomous Vehicles," *Lyft Level 5*, September 23, 2020.

115 Ibid.

similar to ethernet cables for home Wi-Fi units, but they are capable of handling huge amounts of data moving at incredibly fast speeds. The central computer has high-bandwidth input controllers and GPUs which allow the computer to process all of the data.[116]

After the central computer processes all of the data, delays or lagging performance may be dangerous and must be mitigated as much as possible. Thus, the computer runs on a type of time-critical operating system called a Real Time Operating System, or RTOS. A specific RTOS called a robot operating system, or ROS, sends signals from the central computer to a gateway module.[117]

This gateway module is specific to one particular type of vehicle and acts as a gatekeeper in protecting signals going to the actuators that make the car move. The gateway module is a vital part of safety and performance in preventing unintended signals or electromechanical behavior. It knows the code for how the gear shift selector, steering wheel, accelerator, and so on talk to each other. It is the only module allowed to send signals to the vehicle's driving actuators to brake, turn left, or accelerate.[118]

Essentially, in this system, data from the cameras and other sensors is sent to a central computer where it is analyzed by path planning algorithms. It is then sent through a series of computers or computing devices until it reaches the gateway module. The gateway module is specific to each vehicle. A Ford Fusion, Chevy Cruise, or any other vehicle

---

116 Chris Angelini, "Security on the road: Locking down tomorrow's connected vehicles," *VentureBeat*, September 13, 2019.

117 Ibid.

118 Ann Steffora Mutschler, "Vehicle Communications Network is Due for Overhaul," *Semiconductor Engineering*, May 7, 2020.

would have a different gateway module specific to that particular vehicle. The module then sends signals to the brakes, steering wheel, accelerator, and so on, depending on what the case requires it to do. An analogy for this system would be the cerebral cortex sending signals through the central nervous system to the legs to stop, move faster, or turn left.

To summarize, the autonomous driving system, the camera, LiDAR sensor, radar, and ultrasonic sensors represent the "eyes" of the vehicle. These "eyes" send data to neural networks which are trained to recognize patterns from files stored in the computer's hard drive. The neural networks then match those patterns. This system is known as a deep learning neural network.

The vehicle knows about itself by sensors, such as GPS, IMU, gyroscopes, and sensors on the wheels. This allows it to know where it is in relation to all of the objects it perceives through the deep learning system.

The data received through the deep learning neural network is sent to a central computer where it is analyzed by path planning algorithms. It then passes through a series of computers or computing units until it reaches a gateway module. The gateway module sends all of this information to different vehicle actuators (steering wheel, brakes, accelerator, et cetera).

All of these processes happen at the same time, or as near to the same time as possible, in order for the vehicle to react to the road as fast as possible and drive safely. The question then becomes how fast is fast enough to be as safe or safer than a human driver? After all, this is the goal of all of the autonomous vehicle companies in both the US and China.

Researchers at MIT published a study in the *Journal of Experimental Psychology: General* in August 2019. In this study, they found humans need roughly three hundred ninety to six hundred milliseconds to detect and avoid a hazard on the road if given only a single glance at the road. Younger drivers were able to detect and react to hazards faster than older drivers. This created the time disparity of participants in the study.[119]

Lead author Benjamin Wolfe described the simulation in the study, saying, "You're looking away from the road, and when you look back, you have no idea what's going on around you at first glance." Unlike other studies that gave participants a view of the road before a hazard is introduced, this simulation sought to replicate, as closely as possible, a situation in which a hazard emerges out of nowhere. People are not given time to prepare and must simply react to the hazard on the road.[120]

A delay of less than a second could mean the difference between life and death. This must be the standard for which to judge the maturity of the autonomous driving "central nervous system" technology. Everyone in the industry says safety is the number one priority.

The computer "brain" of the autonomous vehicle must have incredible processing power to avoid a collision in under seven hundred milliseconds. This would create incredible stress on any system regardless of how developed that system may be. However, creating safer vehicle transportation is essential. Over one hundred people die in traffic accidents every day in the US alone, and over 1.3 million people die worldwide. Most of these deaths can be attributed to human

---

119 Rob Matheson, "Study shows how fast humans react to road hazards," *MIT News*, August 7, 2019.

120 Ibid.

error such as speeding, fatigue, or distracted and drunk driving.[121]

Computers have the advantage over human drivers in that, if their artificial intelligence is designed and tested enough, they do not get distracted, do not experience fatigue, and never get drunk. Their current processing power will only allow them to drive autonomously under certain conditions and with a high-definition map of the roads already stored in the vehicle's hard drive. Increasing the number of microchips to improve processing performance would also be a problem because the computers would get too hot, particularly if the chips are forced to process the massive amounts of data necessary for autonomous driving.

Either a new cooling system would need to be developed or the vehicles would need to connect to roadside sensors or cloud computing services to drive autonomously in different areas. These infrastructure projects will be discussed in the chapter on China's efforts to build "New Infrastructure" projects.

I have criticized the US for failing to create both laws governing autonomous vehicles and safety standards. However, the legal process cannot be rushed. New technological innovations are still being developed. Creating safety standards for autonomous vehicles that are too rigid to gain permission to drive on public roads could significantly hinder their machine learning systems' ability to mature. Restrictions that are too lenient could lead to a massive deployment of vehicles still in their adolescent stage of technological development. This situation would be unsafe and hurt the industry in the

---

121 Brian Beltz, "100+ Car Accident Statistics for 2020," *Safer America*, October 25, 2018.

long term. The brains of autonomous vehicles are no longer children, but they must still be allowed to learn. A balance must be struck between too strict and too lenient regulations.

At the beginning of this chapter, I discussed that teams of engineers were attempting to make autonomous vehicles run before they learned to walk. This resulted in the destroyed vehicles from the first DARPA Grand Challenge in 2004. While there were some improvements by the vehicles in the subsequent challenges, their autonomous driving systems' "central nervous systems" were still in the infancy stages of their development.

Today, the system has reached its teenage years. The autonomous vehicle still cannot travel outside of the range of its map. However, the deep learning system allows it to better perceive the world around it. The GPS, IMU, and other sensors on the vehicle also allow it to know itself more, what direction it is headed in, and at what speed. The vehicle can now jog slowly on their paths as long as it has a map. Assuming research and development continue at their current pace, or the pace accelerates, the future looks bright for them to increase their speed and move even further in the coming months and years.

Furthermore, the scene portrayed at the beginning of this chapter depicts the fear of many people that they do not have control over the actual driving. This chapter demonstrates that there is human input at every stage of the autonomous vehicle design, development, production, and even monitoring after the vehicles have been deployed. This system is not perfect, but autonomous vehicle companies in both the US and China are striving to make it as close to perfect as possible. A safer driving future depends on it.

The next section describes several key companies and the CEOs dealing with the technological difficulties of making a safe autonomous vehicle. These companies include the industry leaders Waymo, Uber, and Tesla. Other than addressing the technological difficulties laid out in this chapter, these companies also must deal with the uphill battle to gain the trust and acceptance of people in the US. Several new business models are also introduced to make autonomous vehicles commercially viable and profitable for these companies.

PART 2:

MAIN PLAYERS IN THE US AND ROAD TO ACCEPTANCE

CHAPTER 6

JOHN KRAFCIK AND WAYMO: THE "BORING" COMPANY THAT LEADS THE RACE IN THE US

WAYMO IS NOT GOOGLE...ANYMORE: THE HISTORY OF GOOGLE'S PUSH FOR AUTONOMOUS VEHICLES

"First thing I want to mention, we are not Google. We are not a car company. We're also not a self-driving car company. Rather, we are a technology company, and we're building the world's most experienced driver and we call it the Waymo driver and it's our mission to make it simple and easy for people and things to move around the world."[122]

JOHN KRAFCIK, CEO OF WAYMO

122 *Waymo*, "2019 IAA Frankfurt Auto Show Remarks by John Krafcik," October 11, 2019, video. 15:41.

This statement by John Krafcik was made at the 2019 IAA Frankfurt Auto Show. Krafcik, the CEO of Waymo, has also emphasized this point in other interviews. Many people's impression of Waymo is that it is a subsidiary, self-driving car company of Google. To understand what John Krafcik is referring to when he says Waymo is a technology company, it is necessary to examine his statement one step at a time. What does he mean when he says Waymo is not Google? How is Waymo not a self-driving car company, or even a car company?

This chapter seeks to emphasize the importance of experience in developing autonomous vehicles. This is true for the vehicles themselves through years of testing the automated driving system's deep learning algorithms. But it is also true for the CEOs in charge of these companies. John Krafcik was a veteran in the automotive industry for decades before he became CEO of Waymo. He has used his knowledge and expertise to make a technological and business plan that he hopes will ensure Waymo will be the leading autonomous vehicle company in the US and the company all others are judged against. This is true in China and the US. Waymo leads the US in its effort to win the race for autonomous vehicles.

As mentioned in my chapter on dissecting the "brain" of the autonomous vehicle, the DARPA Grand Challenges from 2004 to 2007 featured teams from research laboratories, companies, and universities. These teams attempted to drive a vehicle with no driver around a track to win a monetary prize.[123] Google took note. The initial stage of autonomous vehicle development was conducted at Google's highly

123 Alex Davies, "Inside the Races That Jump-Started the Self-Driving Car," *Wired*, November 18, 2017.

secretive X lab. The work was led by Sebastian Thrum, a Stanford University professor who was the founder of the autonomous vehicle. He and his Stanford University research team won two million dollars in the 2005 DARPA Grand Challenge for driving one hundred thirty-two miles in the desert without a driver.[124]

Google faced a problem in this early stage of needing to justify being a pioneer in the field of autonomous vehicles. Google needed to reassure its employees and investors that a project requiring billions of dollars and thousands of skilled computer engineers, automotive engineers, financial and marketing analysts, litigation and compliance lawyers, and public relations would be profitable. The project would also not be profitable for the foreseeable future. Google was the ideal place to explore new technologies, however, because that is the goal of its secretive X labs.

The behind-the-scenes work of developing the algorithms for the deep learning system was done at the X lab. Six Toyota Priuses and one Audi TT were equipped with GPS, LiDAR sensors, radar, cameras, and the Google self-driving computer system. The cars began to drive through Mountain View, California.[125] For its first in a long series of milestones, these Google cars drove one hundred forty thousand miles by 2010, only one year after the project began.[126]

The project continued in silence for several years until April 2014. Google announced in a statement that its tech could now handle thousands of urban driving simulations.

---

124 Avery Hartmans, "How Google's self-driving car project rose from a crazy idea to a top contender in the race toward a driverless future," *Business Insider*, October 23, 2016.

125 Ibid.

126 Ibid.

These simulations had previously troubled the project's computer engineers.[127] The company's silence can be attributed to the fact that there was little news to report, other than early milestones by their relatively small fleet of vehicles.

This is especially true when you consider Waymo recently passed twenty million miles of driving autonomously on public roads.[128] Part of the reason for the silence could also be due to computer engineers coding algorithms for the significantly more difficult driving conditions in dense urban areas. In cities, there are pedestrians who jaywalk, distracted and drunk drivers who drive through stop signs or red lights, and people riding bicycles who stray out of bike lanes and onto the road. The work to code the car to make it safe when driving in all driving conditions is an arduous and lengthy process.

Wired ran a story on the enormous Google X lab, which was later renamed X labs in an article. Astro Teller, the captain of Moonshots, described the building as akin to Willy Wonka's chocolate factory. The facility itself, a former mall, is gigantic. Robots drive around the halls, stopping to sort through recycle baskets, and autonomous vehicles drive around outside. Stratospheric balloons hang in the rafters of the lobby and broadcast internet signals to remote areas that hang in the rafters of the lobby. The lab's goal is to invent "moonshots"—to try to solve humanity's greatest problems by inventing radical new technologies. This is similar to what I mentioned in the introduction.[129]

---

127 Ibid.

128 Aaron Pressman, "Waymo Reaches 20 Million Miles of Autonomous Driving," *Fortune*, January 7, 2020.

129 Oliver Franklin-Wallis, "Inside X, Google's top-secret moonshot factory," *Wired*, February 17, 2020.

Not content to rely on a stable of Toyota Priuses, which were later changed to Lexus 450h SUVs, the workers at the X lab wanted to make their own vehicle to test and eventually market for their next "moonshot." During Google's Code Conference in May 2014, it unveiled a fully functioning prototype of an autonomous vehicle called the "Firefly." The small, bubble-shaped car had no steering wheel and no brake or gas pedals. The car was turned on by pushing a button. The car had custom sensors and computers to perform all of the necessary driving functions. The Firefly had the appearance of a space pod and could only be described as "cute." When Google debuted this vehicle at the conference, they told everyone they would cap the car's maximum speed at twenty-five miles per hour, and it would only be used as a test vehicle.[130]

Because of these restrictions, Google had no intention of commercializing the Firefly or for it travelling far from the X labs. Also, according to Technical Program Manager Brian Jee, "Those (the Fireflies) were actually just level four." He then clarified this remark, saying, "Sure, they didn't have a steering wheel or pedals, but they were limited to their mapped area...they were geo-fenced to a specific area." These "moonshot" Fireflies were "cute," but Google did not want to be known as a gimmicky company with quirky products. It was time to move forward with their autonomous vehicle project.

Many of the original executives and some of the core team of engineers and other staff members at Google's self-driving car project were part of the original teams from the DARPA

---

130 Avery Hartmans, "How Google's self-driving car project rose from a crazy idea to a top contender in the race toward a driverless future," *Business Insider*, October 23, 2016.

Grand Challenges. However, those people began to leave the Google team, such as former leader of the autonomous vehicle team Sebastian Thrun, Carnegie Melon professor Chris Urmson whose team won the 2007 Urban Challenge, and Anthony Levandowski, who built the first autonomous motorcycle.[131] The remaining team of engineers continued to work on coding the automated driving system and running road tests. However, the company needed to move on from the Firefly (which it finally did officially on July 11, 2017), and also to move beyond the engineers from the infancy of the autonomous vehicle industry.[132]

In September 2015, Google hired former top Hyundai and Ford executive John Krafcik as CEO of the autonomous vehicle project. An established and well-respected businessman, Krafcik would give the program credibility with major auto manufacturers in Detroit and around the world. Krafcik's decades of experience in the auto industry would also be vital as the company moved from the X labs to towns and cities across the country. With his experience as a CEO of Hyundai and top executive at Ford, Krafcik also had the experience to eventually market and commercialize the project's autonomous vehicles.[133]

Not long after Krafcik was hired as the CEO, in October 2015 Google offered the first driverless ride on public roads in Austin, Texas. The autonomous vehicle had no test driver and transported Steve Mahan safely to his destination. Mahan is

---

131 Heather Kelly, "Google loses lead self-driving car engineer Chris Urnson," *CNN Business*, August 5, 2016.

132 Matt McFarland, "Waymo retires its cute self-driving car prototype," *CNN Business*, June 13, 2017.

133 Doug Newcomb, "Google Hires Former Hyundai Exec John Krafcik as CEO of Self-Driving Car Project," *Forbes*, September 14, 2015.

legally blind and the former CEO of the Santa Clara Valley Blind Center. This trip is significant because it is the first trip taken with a human passenger without a backup driver. It also gave the project positive publicity. Google's self-driving car project did more than create futuristic cars. It had the potential to make personal transportation possible for a lot of people like me who currently lack the freedom of mobility an autonomous vehicle could provide.[134]

Less than one year later Google also hired Shawn Stewart, a former executive from Airbnb. Stewart specialized in building and upscaling businesses. Hiring Stewart would allow Google to develop a business strategy for its eventual push to commercialize autonomous vehicles.[135] Airbnb represents a new and innovative approach to renting homes. This provides travelers with more travel accommodation options. This book discusses many different business tactics companies will need to use to offset the added cost of producing autonomous vehicles. Hiring Stewart, a man who helped design an innovative and highly successful business model for Airbnb, put Google in a position to design a business strategy for commercializing autonomous vehicles when the technology and legislation would allow them to do so.

Finally, it was time for Google to move out of the laboratory producing "moonshot" projects, to begin testing its vehicles on public roads throughout the country. On December 20, 2016, the project was moved to a completely separate

---

134 Ashley Halsey III, "Blind man sets out alone in Google's driverless car," *The Washington Post*, December 13, 2016.

135 *Reuters*, "Here's Why Google Just Hired This Airbnb Exec," *Fortune*, August 28, 2016.

company under Alphabet, the parent company of Google. It was renamed Waymo, or "a new **way** forward in **mo**bility."[136]

Referring back to Krafcik's quote at the beginning of this chapter, Waymo is not Google. However, Waymo did benefit from the technology in the automated driving system created by the original Google self-driving car project. Waymo also continues to benefit from the funding and research of Google employees today. Therefore, this statement is really only partly accurate. As far as Krafcik's second and third points in the quote, Waymo is also not a self-driving car company, or even a car company after it disbanded its Firefly project.

The next section describes the history of John Krafcik and how he began to focus on turning Waymo into a technology company. The technology in an automated driving system of any autonomous vehicle company is, after all, the most important part in making sure the vehicle drives safely on public roads and highways.

JOHN KRAFCIK'S LEADERSHIP BACKGROUND USHERS IN A NEW DIRECTION FOR WAYMO

John Krafcik was born on September 18, 1961 in Southington, Connecticut. He lived in this small town in Connecticut for the duration of his adolescent and teenage years before he decided to move across the country for his undergraduate degree. Attending Stanford University for his undergraduate degree, he studied mechanical engineering and received his bachelor's degree in 1983.[137]

Krafcik's first job after finishing his degree at Stanford was working at New United Motor Manufacturing, Inc.,

---

136 Daisuke Wakabayashi, "Google's Parent Company Spins off Self-Driving Car Business," *The New York Times*, December 13, 2016.

137 John Krafcik, "John Krafcik," *LinkedIn*, August 25, 2020.

which was the first step in a lifetime of work in the automotive industry. He worked as a quality and manufacturing engineer from 1984 to 1986. In order to move into a more managerial role, Krafcik moved back to the East Coast where he studied for his master's degree in management at MIT.[138]

At MIT, one of the top technological universities in the world, Krafcik was exposed to many new technological developments. This had a profound impact on his later decision to focus on technology in the auto industry at Waymo. This included research work for the Center for Technology, Policy, and Industrial Development.[139]

During and immediately following his studies at MIT, where he graduated in 1988 with a master's degree in management, Krafcik worked under professor James P. Womach. Under Womach's guidance, Krafcik worked at the International Motor Vehicles Program as a lean production researcher and consultant from 1986 to 1990.This job was a formative experience for Krafcik. It was in this role he was able to gain a clear understanding of the challenges of mass-producing high-quality vehicles. In this job, he travelled to and studied ninety manufacturing plants in twenty countries. In his research notes, he compared their productivity and quality. He also compared the different work styles and manufacturing processes that made the factories operate successfully, as well as the practices that could be improved.[140]

---

138 David Undercoffler, "How I Made It: John Krafcik," *Los Angeles Times*, June 7, 2014.

139 John Krafcik, "John Krafcik," *LinkedIn*, accessed August 25, 2020.

140 Gary S. Vasilash, "Cars Without Coffee: When a Vehicle Isn't Driving Him, John Krafcik Takes the Porsche," *Auto Beat*, May 7, 2020.

Krafcik's notes from this work were used by Womach in his book *The Machine That Changed the World.* This was a study on "lean production." This is a term Krafcik patented to refer to a production style he used throughout his career. Lean production is an approach focused on cutting waste while ensuring quality. This approach can be applied to all aspects of vehicle manufacturing from design, to production, to distribution. The aim is to make the business more efficient and responsive to market needs.[141]

Krafcik used "lean production" for his work in the automotive industry, but it can be applied to many different industries to optimize a company's products and allow for companies to pivot toward new markets. For example, few people remember Amazon was once just an online book buying and downloading website for its Kindle device. Now, it is a massive internet conglomerate, after pivoting to fill the demands for customers wishing to shop online. Amazon could meet the demand of a growing customer base while keeping its costs down by partnering with the USPS to deliver goods from its website to customer's homes. Amazon also built distribution centers all over the US to decrease shipping costs.[142]

After gaining recognition for his work for Dr. Womach, Krafcik worked for Ford Motor Company. At Ford, Krafcik held numerous positions. These positions included chief engineer for the Ford Expedition and Lincoln Navigator until 2004. This experience taught Krafcik how to put his concept of lean production to action. As the chief engineer, he was responsible for directing his subordinates at Ford in everything from the

---

141 Ibid.

142 Marc Onetto, "When Toyota met e-commerce: Lean at Amazon," *McKinsey & Company*, February 1, 2014.

design of the vehicles to the manufacturing and production processes. He could lower waste by reducing production costs, identifying cheaper technologies, and relying on automation for more of the vehicle manufacturing process. Krafcik was successful in building vehicles for one of the largest car manufacturing companies in the world for over a decade.[143]

Building on his success at Ford, Krafcik left Ford to become the president and CEO of Hyundai Motor America in 2013. During Krafcik's time as CEO of Hyundai, they posted record sales and increased their market share in the US.[144] Krafcik, a trained engineer, spent a lifetime working for a premier US automaker in Ford.

Krafcik further refined his managerial tactics working for a relatively new company, at least in the US, with Hyundai. He had a relatively short stint at popular online car dealership website TrueCar from April 2014 to September 2015. It was with his next venture as CEO of Google's self-driving car project, later Waymo, that Krafcik would best be able to put his "lean production" model to the test. He was tasked to deliver the best product while reducing the cost for the more expensive autonomous vehicles.

John Krafcik lacks the eccentricities and boisterous predictions of people like Elon Musk, CEO of Tesla. Instead he presents himself as a stately, respectable man. His extensive knowledge and experience in the automotive industry surpasses every other CEO in the autonomous vehicle industry. That knowledge and experience also fuels his desire to make the "Waymo driver," the "brain" of the autonomous vehicle, the most experienced and safe driver in the world.

---

143 John Krafcik, "John Krafcik," *LinkedIn*, accessed August 25, 2020.

144 Park Seung-heon, "Hyundai and Kia Motors record 9% global market share," *Hani*, August 5, 2014.

I had a conversation with author David Kerrigan who wrote a book on the benefits of autonomous vehicles called *Life as a Passenger*. He described his first ride in a ten to twelve passenger autonomous shuttle in Brussels, Belgium. He remembered, "As far as the experience itself, I was like a little child on Christmas morning. I was so excited to be given the opportunity to actually go in a driverless car."

However, he then admitted even though he has been obsessed with autonomous vehicles for the past five years, he got a little bit bored after about a minute. This boredom was actually a sign everything was working well. While I was initially confused by this, he explained, "John Krafcik from Waymo has always said in his interviews that we are doing the hard work so that you guys should be bored."

While Elon Musk likes to make bold predictions about when autonomous vehicles will be ready for the market, Krafcik and Waymo will not be rushed. In the end, he will let the results of what he hopes will be a dramatically safer driving experience in a Waymo vehicle do the talking.

Google, and later Waymo, have been reaching impressive milestones for driving their vehicles on public roads. After Krafcik took over as CEO, however, they began testing their vehicles in areas with different weather conditions and climates. This exposure to different weather patterns would allow the automated driving system to become a better driver. After all, not everywhere is sunny and clear like it is in southern California.

For example, Google added Kirkland, Washington as a test site in February 2016 due to the region's wet weather.[145]

145 "Google now testing self-driving cars in Washington," *MSNBC*, February 4, 2016.

As discussed in the chapter on cameras and LiDAR sensors, rain and fog can impact object recognition, which affects the vehicle's deep learning system. Therefore, the Waymo vehicles need to be able to cope with rainy conditions to be as safe as possible.

Two months later, Google announced it would be testing its vehicles in Arizona. The stated reason for this test pilot in Arizona was to allow Google to understand "how our sensors and cars handle extreme temperatures and dust in the air."[146]

To complete the inclement weather test sites, Google (now Waymo) launched a test site in Novi, Michigan in October 2017. This site was chosen to test Chrysler Pacifica SUVs equipped with the company's autonomous driving system, cameras, and sensors. This site was chosen to determine how the vehicles react to cold conditions as well as snowy and icy conditions on the road.[147]

While Google announced it would begin to test its vehicles in Arizona in April 2016, it had already sent four vehicles to Phoenix to begin mapping the area. Brian Jee discussed the problems mapping causes by explaining, "That's the killer, which is why for Waymo they started for the rider-less pilot (in Arizona) only like a year ago. Only in Chandler, and they're only now slowly expanding it to certain parts of Phoenix."

The expansion of autonomous vehicles will be a slower and more deliberate process than deploying a new conventional vehicle. While Krafcik was right to say Waymo is not Google, it certainly benefitted from the work Google had

---

146 Avery Hartmans, "How Google's self-driving car project rose from a crazy idea to a top contender in the race toward a driverless future," *Business Insider*, October 23, 2016.

147 Ian Thibodeau, "Waymo to test self-driving cars on Novi roads," *The Detroit News*, October 26, 2017.

done previously. The work Google had already done on what would later become the "Waymo driver" gave the autonomous system the needed experience. Krafcik has continued testing the system in all possible conditions to make Waymo the most advanced and safest autonomous vehicle so far, in both the US and China.

JOHN KRAFCIK'S "LEAN PRODUCTION" MODEL MAKES WAYMO THE LEADER IN THE US

Recognizing the technological side of the autonomous vehicle is the most important, Krafcik was able to use his "lean production" strategy to focus exclusively on that. Because of his decades of experience in the automotive industry, he established close ties with many people at top automakers. This allowed him to more easily form partnerships with companies like Chrysler Pacifica, and now Jaguar, for the vehicles themselves. Focusing on only developing the technology allows Waymo to cut costs by not dealing with developing the vehicle itself and all of the added staff that would entail.

As described in my chapter on the short-term benefits of autonomous vehicles for the US, Krafcik focused on autonomous trucking during the COVID-19 pandemic to raise significant funds. He recognized both the technological limitations of being confined to mapped areas for autonomous passenger transport in "robotaxis." He also recognized the political reality in the US that there are far fewer restrictions for transporting goods than people, even in long-haul freight trucks.[148]

---

148 Keith Naughton, "Waymo CEO sees driverless trucks catching on faster than taxis," *Automotive News Europe*, October 29, 2019.

Finally, Krafcik and Waymo have begun to sell their custom-made LiDAR sensors they use on their Waymo vehicles. They will sell the LiDAR sensors to companies outside the autonomous vehicle industry for companies in industries such as security, robotics, and agricultural technologies. These sales will also help Waymo reduce the price of its LiDAR sensors for its vehicles by scaling up production for economies of scale.[149]

The key challenge for Waymo will be safety. According to a poll conducted by AAA in March 2020, American consumers still do not trust self-driving cars to be safer than human drivers.[150] There are reasons to be skeptical about the credibility of a poll. It is conducted by an organization designed to assist human drivers.

Autonomous vehicles represent a dramatically new and different driving experience for American consumers. Therefore, it would make sense there would be some apprehensions. This is particularly true because people fear their lack of direct control over the transportation experience. For example, some people are afraid to fly even though travelling by plane is the safest method of travel. While autonomous vehicles have not yet reached this level of safety, the experience of the passenger with no direct control of the vehicle is analogous to the person sitting in a plane seat.

Accidents involving autonomous vehicles have a disproportionately large impact on people's trust of autonomous vehicles than accidents involving conventional vehicles. While Waymo has not been involved in a fatal collision,

---

149 Kirsten Korasec, "Waymo to start selling standalone LiDAR sensors," *TechCrunch*, March 6, 2019.

150 Matthew Beadham, "Nearly 90% of Americans don't trust self-driving cars," *Shift*, March 6, 2020.

these accidents will happen. Particularly in the US, where accidents involving autonomous vehicles garner significant media attention, industry leaders need to have a strategy for the best way to provide the public with adequate information to understand a particular accident. This is essential to reassuring the public of the overall safety of autonomous vehicles and to protecting the industry as a whole.

Waymo's goal is to create the most experienced driver in its "Waymo driver." They do this by driving their vehicles for more miles on public roads than every other autonomous vehicle company in the world. Waymo has also driven autonomously on public roads for significantly more total miles than all of the different Chinese companies combined. Waymo, represents the best chance for a US company to beat China in deploying autonomous vehicles on a large scale.

Because of the close public-private partnership which has emerged in China in recent years, it is unrealistic to think a company in the US will beat a Chinese company to commercialize their vehicles on a large scale. The goal needs to be to create the most advanced, experienced, and safest vehicles to set the standard for quality throughout the world. According to Krafcik, "You need to have a lot of real-world experience. There's no way to avoid that. You must have it."[151] He hopes because of the Waymo vehicle's experience, a passenger can have a "boring" ride when the vehicles are ready.

---

151 Irina Slav, "Waymo logs in 20 million miles of self-driving," *Talking Biz News*, January 7, 2020.

CHAPTER 7

UBER CREATES EITHER A REVOLUTIONARY NEW FINANCIAL MODEL OR A FLEIT OF FANCY

UBER EMERGES FROM TRAGEDY TO RESTART ITS AUTONOMOUS VEHICLE PROGRAM

On Sunday evening on March 18, 2018, an Uber autonomous test Volvo XC90 SUV struck and killed forty-nine-year-old Elaine Herzberg. She was walking across the street with her bicycle outside of a crosswalk in Tempe, Arizona.[152]

According to the National Transportation Safety Board's (NTSB) report of the incident, the SUV had three sensors—radar, LiDAR, and camera—designed to detect an object and determine its velocity. However, the vehicle could not determine whether Herzberg was a pedestrian and failed to

152 Troy Griggs and Daisuke Wakabayashi, "How a Self-Driving Uber Killed a Pedestrian in Arizona," *New York Times*, Mach 21, 2018.

determine her path and velocity. According to the report, "The system did not include a consideration for jaywalking pedestrians." Computer engineers at Uber failed to program this very common "edge case" scenario into the system's driving algorithm and this failure resulted in a woman's death.[153]

There was a backup driver behind the wheel who could have taken control of the car. The report mentions 1.2 seconds before the crash, the system recognized Herzberg as a bicycle and not a pedestrian. By then it was too late to safely brake and avoid a collision. According to *The Arizona Republic*, Rafaela Vasquez was watching an episode of *The Voice* on her cell phone while operating the vehicle.[154]

Uber CEO Dara Khosrowshahi tweeted his condolences the following day. He wrote, "Some incredibly sad news out of Arizona. We're thinking of the victim's family as we work with local law enforcement to understand what happened."[155]

Uber offered to pay for the victim's funeral, but this was a weak statement of regret. It never mentioned her name and described the accident like a PR news release with little emotion or believable empathy for her family. This fatal accident badly damaged the American public's already shaky trust in autonomous vehicles. It brought up many questions about civil and criminal liability as well as whether the vehicle itself was safe enough to be on the road.

---

153 Phil McCausland, "Self-Driving Uber car that hit and killed woman did not recognize that pedestrians jaywalk," *NBC News*, November 9, 2019.

154 Ibid.

155 Marcel Schwantes, "Uber CEO Sent This Tweet After a Self-Driving Vehicle Killed a Pedestrian Today. Here's Where It Went Wrong," Inc.com, March 19, 2018.

Almost a year later, in early March 2019, the Yavapai County Attorney's Office prosecutors declared Uber as a corporation did not commit a crime in the fatal crash.[156] However, on August 27, 2020 prosecutors from the neighboring Maricopa County, Arizona charged Ms. Vasquez with criminal negligence.[157] She appeared in court for the first time on September 15, 2020 and the trial is set to take place in February 2021.[158]

After the crash, Uber suspended its autonomous vehicle testing on public roads for nine months. Herzberg's family chose not to sue Uber, which is a welcome sign for companies in the autonomous vehicle industry. However, they did sue the city of Tempe for ten million dollars. This lawsuit could have long-term implications for the industry. Cities might not want to risk losing millions of dollars in lawsuits by allowing autonomous vehicles on their public roads.[159]

This incident also raises questions about the lack of federal regulations and safety standards. Unfortunately, these are still open questions today. According to Ethan Douglas, senior policy analyst for *Consumer Reports,* "We hope Uber has cleaned up its act, but without mandatory standards for self-driving cars, there will always be companies out there that skimp on safety."[160]

---

156 Ray Stern, "Prosecutor: No Crime by Uber in Self-Driving Death; Crash Still Under Scrutiny," *Phoenix New Times*, March 8, 2019.

157 Aarian Marshall, "Why Wasn't Uber Charged in a Fatal Self-Driving Car Crash?," *Wired*, September 17, 2020.

158 Rory Cellan-Jones, "Uber's self-driving operator charged over fatal crash," *BBC*, September 16, 2020.

159 Tim Gallen, "Arizona, Tempe sued by family of woman killed by self-driving Uber vehicle," *The Business Journals*, March 20, 2019.

160 Jeff Plungis, "What Uber's Fatal Self-Driving Crash Can Teach Industry and Regulators," *Consumer Report,* November 19, 2019.

Bills have been introduced since this incident in both the US House and Senate to create federal safety regulations for autonomous vehicles. However, neither bill has been passed to enact the laws. Therefore OEMs, universities, and other autonomous vehicle companies are forced to deal with a patchwork system of many different state and local laws which form a confusing and occasionally contradictory regulatory framework.

This chapter discusses Uber's turn to autonomous vehicles to become profitable. It describes the safety standards enacted by Uber in response to the first, and only, fatal collision involving an autonomous vehicle in the US. Uber has also encouraged other companies in the industry to adopt standards for safety in the absence of federal regulations. Finally, this chapter outlines the innovative new financial model Uber's CEO Dara Khosrowshahi has proposed to finance the company's autonomous vehicle fleet. Because of the media attention related to accidents involving autonomous vehicles, companies in the industry need to be more proactive in demonstrating their commitment to safety. A more coherent and unified approach will be necessary in the future for the autonomous vehicle industry to succeed.

FROM AN IRANIAN EXILE TO THE CEO OF UBER, THE WORLD'S LARGEST RIDE-HAILING PLATFORM

Uber had the right man to navigate through the difficulties of the fatal accident with their CEO Dara Khosrowshahi. This was not the first time he had to deal with scandal and disruption to his life. He was born on May 28, 1969 to a wealthy family in Iran. His family founded the Alborz Investment Company. Under his father, this company became an investment conglomerate involved in pharmaceuticals, chemicals, food, distribution, packaging, trading, and services.[161]

In 1978, when Dara was only nine years old, and one year before the Iranian Revolution, his father was targeted because of his wealth. His mother decided to flee the country with Dara. They were forced to leave everything behind. After the Iranian Revolution, Alborz was nationalized, leaving their family with no money.[162]

His family first fled to southern France. They wanted to eventually return to Iran because Dara's father thought the Iranian Revolution would fail. When the revolution did not fail, the Khosrowshahi family moved to the US and lived with Dara's uncle in Terrytown, New York. Dara achieved his first academic success when he was admitted to Brown University. He graduated from Brown University in 1991 with a BS in electrical and electronics engineering.[163]

His degree was in electrical engineering, but Khosrowshahi chose not to become an engineer or develop new electronics technology. Instead, he followed in his father's footsteps and joined Allen & Company as an investment analyst. There he advised his clients about their respective business.[164]

Khosrowshahi continued to work as a business and financial consultant and was later promoted to senior executive positions at the companies he worked for. His meteoric rise

---

161 Ashley Stewart, "Evolution of a dealmaker: Expedia CEO Dara Khosrowshahi is PSBJ's Executive of the Year," *Puget Sound Business Journal*, December 9, 2016.

162 David Streitfeld and Nellie Bowles, "Uber's CEO Pick, Dara Khosrowshahi, Steps Into Brighter Spotlight," *The New York Times*, August 28, 2017.

163 Ibid.

164 Minda Zetlin, "Expedia Chief Dara Khosrowshahi Will Be Uber's Next CEO. Here's What We Know About Him," Inc.com, August 28, 2017.

in the business community continued when he was promoted to CEO of Expedia in 2005. Ten years later, recognizing Expedia's gross value of its hotel and other boking services more than quadrupled from the time he took over as CEO, he was given ninety million dollars in stock options to keep him at the company.[165]

His work in investment would prove to be invaluable later in Khosrowshahi's life when he devised a plan to finance Uber's autonomous vehicle fleet. His early work as an analyst exposed him to many different business and financial models to advise both small and large companies. His work as CEO of Expedia gave him experience leading a global company. The company provides consumers with a way to make reservations for hotel, airline travel, and car rentals, all from one location. Expedia gave him the experience of optimizing the business-to-consumer strategy that would make him ideally suited to take over as Uber's CEO.

Khosrowshahi joined Uber as their new CEO in August 2017. Why would he leave Expedia, where he had so much success? Maybe he was bored with his current job and wanted a new opportunity, or to take on a new challenge. Or maybe the 45.3-million-dollar salary plus forty million dollars in stocks was just too enticing to ignore. Whatever the case may be, he was entering a situation requiring all of his training and skill for the company to survive.[166]

Following allegations of widespread sexual misconduct and discrimination in Uber's executive offices, their former CEO and founder Travis Kolanick stepped down.

---

165 "Uber picks Dara Khosrowshahi as its new boss," *The Economist*, September 2, 2017.

166 Katie Root, "New Uber CEO may get $200 million," *TechCrunch*, August 28, 2017.

Khosrowshahi claimed Uber's "moral compass" was missing under Kolanick's leadership. Khosrowshahi then appeared in ad campaigns and worked tirelessly to regain the public's trust and plan for the company's future.[167]

Uber's switch to autonomous vehicles was still in its early test stages at that time. From a business planning point of view, the idea of this switch was appealing considering the money that could be saved by not needing a driver in the vehicle. However, this idea was controversial with people worried about autonomous vehicle's impact on the potential job losses of the ride-hailing and delivery truck drivers.

Even potential passengers would need to be convinced as well. I interviewed Karolina Chachulska, director of customer experience and growth at Info Edge. She said companies should first focus on near-term use cases like for food and grocery delivery with Uber Eats. She mentioned using a "robotaxi" would probably need to wait because "human expectations are way, way higher. Especially since most of the Lyft and Uber drivers are really good at getting us from point A to point B." This was a sentiment shared by several other people I interviewed for this book.

As a business model, the decision to turn to autonomous vehicles does make sense for Uber in the long term. Khosrowshahi began to plan for this future after he re-established the company's "moral compass." He also needed to resolve the year-long legal dispute surrounding the hiring of former-Waymo executive Anthony Levandowski and allegations of intellectual property theft. A settlement was reached after five days in court in February 2018. The

---

167 Matthew J. Belvedere, "'Moral compass' was off at Uber under co-founder Kolanick, says new CEO Dara Khosrowshahi," *CNBC*, January 23, 2018.

agreement favored Waymo. Uber guaranteed never to use Waymo hardware or software intellectual property in any of its future vehicles. Uber would also pay Waymo 0.34 percent of its equity, valued at approximately two hundred forty-five million dollars. While this was a blow to Uber, it was not as bad as the billion-dollar settlement Waymo sought initially.[168]

UBER'S EFFORT TO CREATE A SAFETY CULTURE AND INDUSTRY STANDARDS

After eight months of not testing its autonomous vehicles on public roads following the fatal collision, Uber released a safety report. The report stated that since the accident, Uber engineers were working on "reducing the latency," or the delay between when an object is recognized and when an action is taken by the vehicle. Khosrowshahi also said there is pressure for companies to stay silent about their technology in this highly competitive push to develop and produce autonomous vehicles. Uber wanted to join with its competitors to find ways to "measure and demonstrate" autonomous vehicle performance. He also said he hopes to encourage "a culture of transparency rooted in safety" within the autonomous vehicle industry.[169]

Was this just pandering or did this indicate a genuine desire to reform Uber and the industry's strategy an attitude toward safety? The report and the statements from Khosrowshahi were vague, so it really was not clear.

---

168 Aarian Marshall, "Uber and Waymo Abruptly Settle For $245 Million," *Wired*, July 9, 2018.

169 Michael Laris, "'Raising the bar': Uber details shortcomings in self-driving car that killed pedestrian," *The Washington Post*, November 2, 2018.

It wasn't until I listened to two plenary discussions by people from Uber's Advanced Technology Group (ATG) at the 2020 Automated Vehicle Symposium (AVS) from July 28 to 31, 2020 that I learned about the changes Uber made following the fatal accident. Christopher SanGiovanni, director of organizational safety management at Uber ATG, discussed the massive organizational changes made by Uber to create a "safety culture" in the "Lessons Learned from Uber Crash" plenary discussion on July 28, 2020.[170]

Mr. SanGiovanni described how the accident was devastating to Uber as an organization. They needed to dig deep, have a lot of introspection, examine any contributing factors for the accident, and keep the focus entirely on themselves. What organizational failures led to this accident and how can they make changes to try to avoid similar failures in the future?[171]

Uber conducted an entire safety review with external support from the NTSB, the same government organization which created the report from the fatal collision. The review was very extensive and examined everything from the organizational structure, who reports to who, down to the safety operator in the driver's seat during test runs of the autonomous vehicles on public roads.[172]

For organizational changes, Uber fostered a culture of openness and transparency with issues related to safety. The safety department became more proactive in gathering data related to safety and there was a continued educational

170 Christopher SanGiovanni, Ensar Becic, and Kristin Kingsley, "Lessons Learned from Uber Crash," (lecture, *2020 Automated Vehicles Symposium*, virtual, July 27, 2020).

171 Ibid.

172 Ibid.

emphasis on safety for every department within the organization. The safety department was made independent from the Operational Safety Division and communicated any concerns directly to the CEO.[173]

Not only was training increased and another vehicle operator added to the autonomous vehicle during test runs on public roads, but their name was changed as well. Vehicle operators were now referred to as "mission specialists." This led to greater pride in their work, more compensation, and they received the same perks and benefits as other employees. Similar to aviation, these "mission specialists" would go on "missions" instead of test runs and were given "command authority" like a pilot.[174]

Not related to the organizational changes focused on improving safety for Uber ATG, but still vital, was the emphasis on testing on public roads. According to Mr. SanGiovanni, "Prior to the crash, the goal was to log as many miles on public roads as you can." Following the crash, however, he stated they would only test the vehicles on public roads when it was absolutely necessary to prove the testing was done in computer simulations and on private tracks.[175]

Testing procedures are another area of weakness in the policy framework governing autonomous vehicles in the US. California alone has approved sixty-six permits for autonomous vehicle testing on public roads. NHTSA has twelve policy guidelines for testing on public roads, but compliance is cursory and there are no safety parameters. Submission of safety reports is also voluntary and there have only been

---

173 Ibid.

174 Ibid.

175 Ibid.

twenty-three submissions. The detail of these submissions also varies based on the company submitting them.[176]

With no federal mandates for testing, Uber and other companies have pushed for the adoption by companies of Underwriters Laboratories (UL) 4600. I became aware of UL 4600 in another plenary discussion at the AVS 2020 called "UL4600: Industry Approach and Applications." UL 4600 creates a robust standard for a safety case-based approach to testing. According to Director of Uber ATG Safety Standards Chris Mullen, this approach is their goal and he states, "The safety case is a structured case that ensures that the risk of harm has been reduced to an acceptable level."[177]

Autonomous vehicle technology is still relatively new. ISO 26262 functional safety standards describe benchmarks for the functional safety of the technology itself.[178] For example, as Brian Jee described, the automotive ethernet cables are a very robust technology that can effectively send massive amounts of data at incredibly fast speeds. Therefore, it would meet the standards of the ISO 26262 functional safety standard.

UL 4600 does not preclude companies from following other safety standards but serves as an additional benefit to existing standards. It creates robust standards for testing based on a continuous feedback loop. It is relatively unaffected by large changes in technology, even though it is still updated every year. Ms. Mullen indicated Uber ATG uses UL 4600 and Uber pushes for other companies to use it as

---

176 Ibid.

177 Benjamin Lewis, Chris Mullen, Junko Yoshida, and Philip Koopman, "UL4600: Industry Approach and Applications" (panel discussion, *2020 Automated Vehicle Symposium*, virtual, July 27, 2020).

178 Richard Bellairs, "What is ISO 26262? An Overview of ISO 26262 and ASIL," *Perforce*, January 3, 2019.

well. They want to create standardization of testing currently lacking within federal regulations. This would build the public's trust in the technology and create more certainty for industries such as the auto insurance industry.[179]

The organizational emphasis on safety by Uber, the independence of the safety department with direct lines of communication to the CEO, and the changes to the vehicle operators indicated Uber's complete overhaul of the "safety culture" throughout every aspect of the organization. Since stringent federal guidelines and regulations were absent, the next step would be to attempt to ensure these, or similar, changes were adopted by companies in the industry as a whole. After re-establishing Uber's "moral compass" and overhauling the organizational structure to create a "safety culture" following the fatal collision, Khosrowshahi would need to create the financial structure to support Uber's autonomous vehicle ambitions.

UBER DEBATES HOW IT CAN BECOME PROFITABLE

Khosrowshahi spent his first year after taking over as CEO of Uber defensive driving. He had to deal with the scandals of his predecessor, the lawsuit, and the fatal collision. He was not in a position to put his foot on the accelerator and make statements about the imminent arrival of autonomous vehicles, nor is that his temperament.

He said the main difference between Musk's approach of predicting the arrival of autonomous vehicles as early as 2020 and his would be the expected timing. Khosrowshahi said it could be five to ten years before autonomous vehicles are

---

179 Benjamin Lewis, Chris Mullen, Junko Yoshida, and Philip Koopman, "UL4600: Industry Approach and Applications" (panel discussion, *2020 Automated Vehicle Symposium*, virtual, July 27, 2020).

mass produced and deployed.[180] The question would be how long Uber could keep funneling research and development money to develop autonomous vehicles, given their already precarious financial situation.

I spoke with a vice president of an insurance carrier about issues related to insuring autonomous vehicles. Talking about autonomous vehicles, she said, "I don't know how quickly this will be a norm in society." She did leave the door open for them to arrive on the roads in some capacity, saying, "I do think that there are plenty of people who will sign up for these types of vehicles, (but) they are going to be expensive vehicles." She added that ultimately it would also depend on where people live. The initial use case, because of the increased price tag, would likely be autonomous taxis. Therefore, Uber would face increased competition, assuming every other autonomous vehicle company used the taxi model for an initial roll-out.

Khosrowshahi did discuss the pressure of developing a safer vehicle alternative because of the nearly forty thousand deaths every year related to traffic accidents with human drivers in the US alone. The status quo could not continue, but he did mention those type of numbers for a robot driver would not be tolerated. Like Elon Musk, he did make a similar grandiose sounding prediction when he argued autonomous vehicles are "part of the solution" to ending individual vehicle ownership in the US. He only lacked the timetable Musk frequently adds to his statements. This was a remarkable statement considering the US has over one hundred years of individual car ownership.[181]

---

180 Lora Kolodny, "Elon Musk is wrong on robotaxi timing, Uber CEO Dara Khosrowshahi says," *CNBC*, May 10, 2019.

181 Catherine Clifford, "Uber's CEO: 'We are absolutely committed to self-driving cars," *MSNBC*, April 13, 2018.

Khosrowshahi's primary task as CEO of Uber would be to make Uber profitable. Uber has had quarterly losses practically from the moment it was founded. According to a study by *Reuters* in 2017, Uber customers paid only forty-one percent of the actual cost of the trip. The report was conducted after Uber released some financial documents as a then-private company. Uber had losses of $708 million that quarter.[182]

With a $1.3 billion loss in the third quarter of 2019, it had gotten worse instead of better. Part of the problem is subsidies Uber offers to first-time users of the mobile app, and occasionally offers to long-time users as well. Uber also faces increased competition for its ride-hailing platform from Lyft and from GrubHub for its food delivery app, Uber Eats.[183]

Khosrowshahi is, first and foremost, a businessman and dealmaker. After he joined Uber, Khosrowshahi focused on cutting costs. Uber sold operations in Russia and Southeast Asia for stakes in local ride-hailing services in 2018. Uber did the same thing to Uber's food delivery business Zomato in India in 2019. India was Uber's most costly delivery market. The cuts continued in 2020 when Uber closed food delivery services in seven countries and fired 3700 people around the world.[184]

Uber's already tenuous financial situation has taken a significant hit during the COVID-19 pandemic. Uber's ride-hailing platform suffered greatly in 2020 with the

---

182 Heather Somerville, "True price of an Uber ride in question as investors assess firm's value," *Reuters*, August 23, 2017.

183 Lauren Feiner, "Uber stock falls after quarterly results bet estimates, but losses topped $1 billion," November 4, 2019.

184 Gerrit De Vynck, Olivia Carville, and Lizette Chapman, "Uber's CEO, a Seasoned Dealmaker, Pursues His Biggest One Yet," *Bloomberg*, May 14, 2020.

company's revenue falling twenty-nine percent from the second quarter of 2019. People travelling less and fear of contracting the coronavirus can explain the substantial drop in the ride-hailing platform. While the ride hailing service has slowed, Uber Eats food delivery service has thrived. Revenue from the Uber Eats food delivery service has more than doubled from May 2019 to May 2020 to $1.2 billion, as opposed to only $790 million for the ride-hailing platform. This was the first time the food delivery platform outgrossed the ride-hailing platform since Uber Eats was first created.[185]

Khosrowshahi made a name for himself at Expedia for being an effective dealmaker and making purchases. When he ran Expedia Group Inc. for more than ten years, he completed forty-one transactions worth $12.7 billion according to data collected by *Bloomberg*. He then reverted back to this formula when facing a steep decline in ridership for Uber's ride-hailing fleet by attempting to purchase Uber's main competitor in the food delivery industry: Grubhub Inc. This announcement of negotiations between Uber and Grubhub was criticized by officials, one of whom called it "pandemic profiteering."[186]

Uber was unable to secure a deal to buy Grubhub, however, and it was sold to Dutch food delivery company Just Eat Delivery for $7.3 billion on June 10, 2020.[187] This was a blow to Uber, which hoped purchasing Grubhub would

---

185 Kate Conger, "Uber's Revenue Craters, as Deliveries Surge in Pandemic," *The New York Times*, August 6, 2020.

186 Gerrit De Vynck, Olivia Carville, and Lizette Chapman, "Uber's CEO, a Seasoned Dealmaker, Pursues His Biggest One Yet," *Bloomberg*, May 14, 2020.

187 Kate Conger, Adam Satariano, and Michael de la Merced, "Just Eat Takeaway to Acquire Grubhub for $7.3 Billion," *The New York Times*, June 10, 2020.

grant it the clear market share lead in food delivery services in the US. However, Khosrowshahi was not finished. He purchased startup Postmates, the tele-operated delivery robot company introduced in chapter two, for $2.65 billion on June 29, 2020.[188]

Even while Khosrowshahi strived to increase Uber Eats' food delivery profits by buying other companies, he never lost sight of his goal to create a fleet of autonomous "robotaxis" to maximize the profit from Uber's ride-hailing platform. The additional cost of autonomous vehicles is a problem every company in the industry must face. Other companies use different methods for reducing the cost of autonomous vehicles, which are discussed in other chapters in this book. Khosrowshahi's financial skill and experience led to Uber creating a revolutionary, but risky, new investment plan.

KHOSROWSHAHI CREATES AN INNOVATIVE NEW FINANCIAL FRAMEWORK FOR ROBOTAXI "FLEITS"

Unlike Didi in China, Uber does not actually own the vehicles in their ride-hailing fleet. To get around the problem of actually owning the fleets of autonomous "robotaxis," Khosrowshahi needed to use his investment experience to identify a solution to this problem. He argued for a system industry experts have nicknamed "Fleits."

Fleits are car fleet investment trusts. This is a variation of Reits, which are real estate investment trusts. Reits own three trillion dollars in property assets in the US alone. Under this investment system, investors would get a share of the fast-growing sector's profits and also a possible tax incentive,

188 Mike Isaac, Erin Griffith, and Adam Satariano, "Uber Buys Postmates for $2.65 Billion," *The New York Times*, July 5, 2020.

such as the one given to Reits. This share had to be negotiated ahead of time but would be approximately six percent funded by the cash flow generated from rides.[189]

Uber would not be responsible for actually owning the fleet of vehicles. The vehicles would be provided by an auto manufacturer and Uber would mainly be responsible for vetting the autonomous software developers of the Fleits companies. This would be similar to the current vetting process for human drivers, which has become substantially more stringent following the fatal collision. However, it would still mean Uber would have to hire and retain a skilled staff of trained computer engineers to effectively judge the quality of different automated driving systems.

For Uber this sounds like the ideal scenario for its autonomous vehicle fleet. However, many challenges make this strategy less attractive to investors in the Fleits. The vehicles would depreciate rapidly, especially if they are used all day and night to maximize profit by having as many rides as possible. Also, if there was no human driver, there would be no one to prevent customer behavior that could damage the vehicle. Having a camera directed at the interior of the vehicle could reduce the risk of people damaging the vehicle. However, that raises privacy concerns about who is watching them and whether this footage will be stored or shared.

The cameras facing the interior of the vehicle might not be much of an issue from a legal perspective. In my talk with the vice president of the insurance carrier, I asked her about the potential risk to a person's privacy if the vehicle is being used as part of an autonomous "robotaxi" fleet. She said, "There's pretty strict privacy laws and data storage laws

---

189 Marketing, "What is a REIT?," *Project Control*, December 1, 2018.

like when companies start to collect information and store information. There are some pretty strict rules and regulations that people have to abide by." Therefore, the cameras could mainly be used for short duration storage or to serve as a warning for riders to behave appropriately in the vehicle.

One issue would be if there was an accident and there was information about the vehicle used for the trial. In this case, she said, "They have to give certain information about the person and that could potentially be an issue if the person is not okay with sharing information." It all depends on the accident. If the person thinks the issue was the fault of the vehicle, then they would want the vehicle manufacturer to share the information. However, if the vehicle manufacturer believes there was a problem with the passenger then they would want to have that information shared. This would most likely require clarification in future legislation, she said.

Individual passengers are not the only people who will need to worry about liability under this new system. Owners of the vehicles would also be subject to potential liability concerns for accidents involving their vehicles. While insurance would diminish the risk of each individual accident, the premiums would increase. These premiums could skyrocket if there are many accidents in which it is deemed the autonomous vehicle was at fault.

While the Herzberg family chose to sue Tempe, Arizona and not Uber, the question of civil liability still has not yet been resolved. Both Uber and vehicle manufacturers could possibly be held liable and be subject to lawsuits in the future. This would include potential liability risk for investors in the Fleits. Unfortunately for Uber, investors do not like risks and uncertainty, and this plan contains both.

Uber has already begun to seek investors for its autonomous vehicle Fleits. One year before it went public, Uber received a five-hundred-million-dollar investment from Toyota for its autonomous vehicle division.[190] Uber went public on the New York Stock Exchange in May 2019 and it was one of the biggest IPOs of the year. A few weeks before Uber went public, they received a billion-dollar investment from the Japanese bank SoftBank and other investors.[191]

Khosrowshahi has bet everything that, by taking the driver out of the picture, this would make Uber profitable. Turning to a radical financial model of autonomous vehicle, Fleits represents his riskiest bet yet. The only other option would be to form a partnership with fleets of autonomous vehicles from a vehicle manufacturer for Uber to purchase its own vehicles. However, this would be expensive and would not necessarily be the easiest route to profitability. Khosrowshahi needs to stop defensive driving and step on the accelerator to gain the needed investors for Uber to start its Fleits, sooner rather than later given Uber's financial woes.

Hiring Khosrowshahi when they did was the right choice for Uber. He knew how to handle adversity from the days of his forced exile from his home country in Iran. He showed resolve in changing the company's work culture after the scandals of his predecessor. His handle on the media right after the fatal crash which killed Elaine Herzberg left much to be desired. However, his response to completely change the organizational structure and work culture to focus on a "safety culture" was admirable. Realizing I only found out

---

190 Greg Bensinger and Chester Dawson, "Toyota Investing $500 Million in Uber in Driverless-Car Pact," *Wall Street Journal*, August 27, 2018.

191 Deirdre Bosa, "Uber announces $1 billion investment into its self-driving car group, weeks before going public," *CNBC*, April 18, 2019.

about these changes over two years later from a speech given at a paid symposium does identify issues with public relations and dealings with the media which should be addressed. People need to be aware of the positive changes the company has made since the accident.

Uber's greatest risk could be a tremendous benefit for autonomous vehicle companies in their initial push to form autonomous "robotaxi" Fleits. This would be a tough sell to potential investors. However, this would mean substantial cost savings and could possibly create a revolutionary new financial model for the industry.

With Uber as the world's leading ride-hailing app, the autonomous vehicle industry in the US is hoping Khosrowshahi's bet on autonomous vehicles succeeds. Not just for developing autonomous vehicles in the US, Uber's global reach presents opportunities to extend America's advantage abroad. This is where the next stage of the autonomous vehicle competition will begin and where the winners will be decided between the US and China. The first step is finding willing financiers in the US.

CHAPTER 8

IS ELON MUSK THE SAVIOR OR VILLAIN OF THE AUTONOMOUS VEHICLE INDUSTRY IN THE US?

THE SAVIOR, OR VILLAIN, OF THE AUTONOMOUS VEHICLE INDUSTRY ARRIVES

Twelve Thai soccer players and their coach hiked into the Tham Luong Nang cave system in northern Thailand on June 23, 2018. After they entered the cave, the cave's entrance was blocked by floodwaters. The floods trapped all of them in a compartment half a mile underground and two-and-a-half miles from the mouth of the cave.[192]

---

192 "The full story of Thailand's extraordinary cave rescue," *BBC News*, July 14, 2018.

A rescue mission was almost inconceivable because there was a tremendous risk of the cave collapsing. This would lead to more people being either trapped or killed in the rescue effort. Millions of people all over the world were riveted, eagerly following any developments of the story in front-page headlines and 24/7 news reports on all of the major news outlets. Divers arrived from England and other countries to join the Thai Navy SEAL team to plan and conduct the extraction of the children and their coach. They would have to travel through the narrow tunnels of the cave, often working in total darkness.[193]

The media attention attracted the attention of billionaire tech titan Elon Musk. He offered to design miniature submarines that could rescue the children. His offer to help was criticized by Vernon Unsworth. He was one of the British divers who had travelled to Thailand to assist with the rescue effort. He called Musk's offer to help with the submarines "a PR stunt" in an interview with CNN.[194]

Unsworth was part of the heroic rescue, which saw the boys finally emerge from the cave in good overall health. Musk could have ignored Unsworth's comments. He and the rest of the team of divers were being adulated for what many considered to be a near-impossible rescue mission. Instead Musk went on the attack, tweeting that Unsworth is a "pedo guy," implying he is a pedophile.[195]

Musk's attack on Unsworth followed a familiar trend, treating the media and anyone critical of him and his companies as the villain. After initially refusing to apologize,

---

193 Ibid.

194 Li Zhou, "Elon Musk and the Thai cave rescue: a tale of good intentions and bad tweets," *Vox*, July 18, 2018.

195 Ibid.

Musk later tweeted on July 18, 2018 that while Unsworth's comments about his desire to help were untruthful, his reply was based on anger. He then made another tweet stating, "His actions against me do not justify my actions against him, and for that I apologize to Mr. Unsworth and to the companies I represent as a leader."[196]

Musk has been a true visionary throughout his career, working at the forefront to develop new industries. His work with Tesla has greatly benefitted both the electric vehicle and autonomous vehicle industries. However, the success or failure of the autonomous vehicle industry in the US may depend on him as the most charismatic public figure in the industry. To do this, he must treat the media less like a villain and more like an advocate for autonomous vehicles.

* * *

Elon Musk was born on July 28, 1971 in Pretoria, South Africa.[197] Spending the early part of his life in South Africa, he briefly attended the University of Pretoria. He then embarked on a journey that took him first to Canada, where he studied at Queen's University.[198] After two years at Queen's University, he transferred to the University of Pennsylvania. There he received a bachelor's degree in economics from the Wharton School and a bachelor's degree in physics from the College of Arts and Sciences.[199]

---

196 Mihir Zaveri, "Elon Musk Walks Back 'Pedo Guy' Attack on That Cave Diver," *The New York Times*, July 18, 2018.

197 Shelbi Ausin, "10 Things You Didn't Know About Elon Musk," *U.S.* News, May 23, 2018.

198 Erik Seedhouse, *SpaceX: Making Commercial Spaceflight a* Reality (New York: Praxis, June 15, 2013) 3.

199 Jaron Zanerhaft, "Elon Musk: Patriarchs and Prodigies," *CSQ*, 2013.

His whirlwind educational journey ended when he attended Stanford University, where he began his PhD in applied physics and material sciences. However, he dropped out after two days and started his business career.[200] It is unclear why his studies as a PhD student were cut short so abruptly. Whatever the reason may be, it was time for him to begin to establish a name for himself as an innovator. He was certainly in the right place at the right time in Silicon Valley during the tech boom of the 1990s.

Musk made a name for himself as an internet pioneer founding and selling two companies during the 1990s.[201] In May 2002, Musk left the world of internet business in favor of space voyage and transportation when he launched SpaceX. SpaceX is an aerospace manufacturer and space transport service.[202]

For voyages much closer to home, Elon Musk joined Tesla, Inc. in 2004. Tesla is an electric vehicle manufacturing company.[203] Other than manufacturing electric vehicles, Musk also created SolarCity, a solar energy services company which is now a subsidiary of Tesla.[204] Musk bet all of his money on what at the time, and perhaps even now, were risky bets. His business vision would be severely tested in the coming years.

Pursuing a new venture would not just be risking millions of dollars on a failed internet venture. Any vehicle or

---

200 "Elon Musk," Bibliography.com, May 26, 2020.

201 Sergei Klebnikov, "8 Innovative ways Elon Musk Made Money Before He Was a Billionaire," *Everyday* Money, August 8, 2017.

202 Emre Kelly, "How Elon Musk took SpaceX from an idea to the cusp of making history," *USA Today*, May 26, 2020.

203 Matt Burns, "A Brief History of Tesla," *TechCrunch*, October 8, 2014.

204 Daniel Gross, "The Miracle of SolarCity," *Slate*, July 31, 2015.

spaceship failure could hurt or kill people. I had a conversation with my friend, a graduate student at Tsinghua University who has been interning for an autonomous vehicle startup in Beijing. He got to drive in a level three autonomous Audi vehicle, saying, "If for some unforeseen consequences I crash into something and someone dies or I die, then Audi is going to get the blame for that, or Tesla for an American example." Even though Tesla was originally just an electric vehicle company, Musk is still risking his money, reputation, and potentially people's lives if there is a mistake with his vehicles.

Educating the public about the benefits of electric vehicles would require Musk to have a favorable relationship with the media. In recent years, Musk has attacked the media in tweets and statements for being "holier than thou," arguing it had lost its credibility and journalists wrote negative stories about Tesla "because they want more page views."[205]

As one of the leading figures in the high-tech world with a massive following of loyal people, Musk has done a wonderful job overall of advancing the cause of both electric vehicles and autonomous vehicles. Attacking the media is counter-productive to his goals both as a businessman and advocate for his passion of autonomous vehicles.

Musk's suspicion and paranoia about the media and all perceived "enemies" is not new. Musk's short temper and outbursts are well-known to current and former employees at Tesla and SpaceX. When asked about his recent outbursts, an employee responded, "It doesn't strike me as some drastic change in his personality."[206]

---

205 Matt Stevens, "Why is Elon Musk Attacking the Media? We Explain. (Also, Give Us a Good Rating!)," *The New York Times*, May 24, 2018.

206 Caroline O'Donovan, Charlie Werzel, and Ryan Mac, "Elon Musk Has Always Been at War With the Media," *BuzzFeed News*, June 21, 2018.

This story does not describe the whole story, either. As of January 2020, Elon Musk has thirty million Twitter followers.[207] Therefore, he has immense power to serve as both an advocate for the industries he represents and as a detractor because of his attacks. Channeling that power would be of great benefit to the autonomous vehicle industry, just as it has proven to be for the electric vehicle industry in the US.

While winning over the media was not something Musk was prepared to focus on, the first step would be to make electric vehicles people would actually want to buy. As I discussed in my chapter on the short-term benefits of autonomous vehicles, they are held to a higher safety standard than human-driven vehicles. Therefore, they attract significantly more media attention than other vehicles regardless of what company makes them.

This chapter will examine the contributions Elon Musk has made to the autonomous vehicles industry. Of perhaps even greater importance, this chapter discusses Musk's polarizing personality. His statements and actions both inform and advocate for autonomous vehicles. However, his statements and actions can also damage the already shaky trust Americans have for autonomous vehicles when he attacks the media, local government, and critics.

TESLA'S AUTOPILOT-ENABLED VEHICLES HIT THE ROAD

Musk's greatest challenge yet would be to make Americans excited about electric vehicles. Even in 2018, only five percent of battery-operated vehicles of all forms accounted for the new car sales. According to a 2019 survey conducted by AAA,

---

207 Clara Linnane, "Yes, Jack Dorsey, Elon Musk does have an idea about how to fix Twitter," *MarketWatch*, January 17, 2020.

forty million Americans said they will buy an electric vehicle for their next car. However, only forty percent believed the majority of cars sold in the US would be electric by 2029.[208]

What accounts for this gap in desire by consumers for electric vehicles and actual purchases? According to Greg Bannon, AAA's director of automotive engineering, "Like other new vehicle technologies, Americans don't have the full story which could be causing the gap between interest and action."[209] The same would also be true for autonomous vehicles. Another explanation could be there are infrastructure constraints with a lack of charging stations or a lengthy charging time for some vehicles. Therefore, Musk had to deal with both a lack of information about electric vehicles and charging infrastructure constraints.

Tesla's first electric vehicle, the Roadster, debuted in 2008 and the most obvious improvement of this car was its sleek, two door sportscar design. The car could also achieve two hundred forty-five miles on a single charge. This was an improvement from previous electric vehicles, such as the tiny, box-shaped Smartcar rental cars. The car could accelerate from zero to sixty miles per hour in less than four seconds. However, despite a federal tax credit of seven thousand five hundred dollars for purchasing an electric vehicle, the Roadster still cost one hundred nine thousand dollars. This would make it outside the price range of most consumers.[210]

---

208 Paul A. Eisenstein, "AAA study finds Americans are warming to electric vehicles, but most aren't ready to buy – at least not yet," *CNBC*, May 9, 2019.

209 Ibid.

210 Aaron Brown, "Here's a look back at the Tesla car that started it all," *Business Insider*, March 30, 2016.

Tesla's next vehicle was the Model S. The Model S was acclaimed by automotive critics for its performance and design. The sedan came with three different battery options with ranges of two hundred thirty-five or three hundred miles per charge. The Model S also offered Tesla's next innovation to the automotive market with its Autopilot option for an additional eight thousand dollars.[211]

The Autopilot feature adds semiautonomous driving for all Model S (and later model) vehicles. One thing to note is Tesla's Autopilot does not make the vehicle completely autonomous. Rather, Autopilot is a suite of automotive systems including lane-centering, adaptive cruise control, self-parking, the ability to automatically change lanes, navigate autonomously on limited access freeways, and the ability to summon the car to and from a parking garage or spot.[212]

There have been drivers who make or appear in YouTube videos who are asleep in the driver's seat or sitting in the backseat while the Tesla vehicle has Autopilot engaged. The vehicle's owner manual clearly states people still need to have their hands on the steering wheel at all times and need to pay attention to the road in case they need to manually take control.[213] Abusing the Autopilot feature is reckless and could lead to fatal accidents.

Tesla has repeatedly claimed driving with Autopilot engaged is safer than a human-driven vehicle, with one accident every three million miles reported. The national

---

211 Andrew J. Hawkins, "How Tesla changed the auto industry forever," *The Verge*, July 28, 2017.

212 Mark Matousek, "The most impressive things Tesla's cars can do in Autopilot," *Business Insider*, January 29, 2018.

213 Laura Kolodny and Michael Wayland, "Watch Tesla drivers apparently asleep at the wheel, renewing Autopilot safety questions," *CNBC*, September 9, 2019.

average is one crash for every four hundred eighty thousand miles driven.[214] However, when accidents do occur involving a Tesla driving with Autopilot engaged, the stories make headlines. People assume Autopilot means the vehicle is fully autonomous. The name itself suggests this. Tesla needs to have clearer advertising campaigns which mention the vehicles are not actually fully autonomous.

Tesla has introduced several key features which will be very important for the autonomous vehicle industry moving forward. Something crucial for the success of autonomous vehicles in both the US and China is Tesla's Over-The-Air (OTA) update system. This system allows Tesla vehicles to download updates wirelessly, as long as they are connected to a Wi-Fi network or data source (4G-LTE, 5G, et cetera).[215]

TESLA'S OTA SYSTEM AND INFRASTRUCTURE IMPROVEMENTS ADDRESS CRUCIAL NEEDS

The OTA system allows Tesla vehicles to update changes to its Autopilot system. These changes could include the layout and appearance of its touchscreen interface and even the range of the system for things like hurricane predictions.[216] The updates for autonomous vehicles will be more frequent and more extensive. These updates will have things like map updates and will be crucial for autonomous vehicles to drive safely on public roads.

When Musk first joined Tesla back in 2004, there were very few public charging stations in the US. The charging

---

214 Fred Lambert, "Tesla Autopilot crash rate increases, but still lower than without Autopilot," *electrek*, January 16, 2020.

215 Alex Brisbourne, "Tesla's Over-The-Air Fix: Best Example Yet of the Internet of Things?," *Wired*, May 25, 2018.

216 Ibid.

stations that did exist were mostly clustered around large cities, such as Los Angeles, San Francisco, Boston, or New York City. Therefore, a person might have to drive possibly five or more miles to charge their vehicle. The first-generation electric outlets would also take significantly longer to fully charge a vehicle than filling up a vehicle with gas.

As of March 2020, there are 78,500 charging outlets in almost twenty-five thousand charging stations in the US. A large portion of these charging stations (6,835 with 28,545 charging outlets) are in California, where there are over six hundred thousand plug-in electric vehicles as of September 2019. The sales of electric vehicles in California were also up eighty-four percent from 2018.[217]

Elon Musk and Tesla have been part of this increase in charging stations. Tesla has built 16,103 Superchargers (outlets with very fast charging speed) at 1,826 charging stations around the world. This includes nine hundred eight charging stations in the US. This is the largest number of stations in any one country or region in the world.[218]

This is significant because Elon Musk recognized there was a problem in the lack of charging stations and fast-charging outlets in the US. He decided to address this problem by having Tesla build this needed infrastructure themselves. He chose to focus on this construction rather than wait for national, state, or local governments to make the investment.

Leaders in the autonomous vehicle industry, like Elon Musk and John Krafcik at Waymo, could work together to

---

217 "Electric Vehicle Charging Network (Stations & Outlets): Charging a Cleaner Tomorrow," *much needed*, May 27, 2020.

218 Connor Huffman, "How Well Does a Tesla Model 4 Work For a Long Trip?," *Car and Driver*, May 22, 2020.

pressure Congress to invest in creating a robust 5G network in the US. They could also work with local governments, infrastructure companies, or other organizations to co-finance smart infrastructure projects. These projects could include things like smart stoplights or roadside cameras. These projects would assist the functioning of autonomous vehicles and allow them to drive more safely. Building these projects is something China has been focusing on. I will describe this in my chapter on Xi Jinping and China's new focus on developing new technology.

I had a talk with Dr. Sven Beiker, the founder and managing director of Silicon Valley Mobility. This is a private consulting company, specializing in business-corporate relations in the automotive industry. He discussed some of the key points about infrastructure that need to be considered for the autonomous vehicle industry to succeed. He said, "Infrastructure needs to be amended now, extended, or adopted to include self-driving vehicles. We need to see who actually finances that infrastructure." He pointed out this could be specific infrastructure companies, vehicle manufacturing companies (like Tesla for its charging infrastructure), and/or the government.

He noted getting the government involved "definitely slows things down, but I think it will not be possible without it." Therefore, companies need to continue to work on making their autonomous vehicles as safe as possible. They may also need to invest in specific smart infrastructure projects themselves. By doing this, they would be following Elon Musk's example at Tesla.

Elon Musk and Tesla have worked to increase people's acceptance of the electric vehicle. They have also introduced them to the potential benefits of autonomous driving with their driver-assistance Autopilot system. However, Elon Musk remains an enigma managing his public persona. He can generate positive publicity for both Tesla and the autonomous vehicle industry by identifying the incredible benefits they can bring society (albeit with questionable predictions about when they will be ready.) However, some of his actions and statements hurt the goodwill he could gain for both Tesla and the industry as a whole.

MUSK'S CONTENTIOUS RELATIONSHIP WITH THE MEDIA CONTINUES TO HINDER HIS GOALS

As demonstrated in the story introduced this chapter, Musk has created controversy from his comments in the past but his tweets in August 2018 almost led to his downfall. On August 7, 2018, Musk tweeted, "Am considering taking Tesla private at $420 (per share). Funding secured."[219]

Musk later reaffirmed it could potentially be the best move. Making Tesla a private commodity, he tweeted, remove the burden of the "pressure from Wall Street expectations." He later emphasized in a tweet that the decision was not final.[220] However, the damage was already done.

These tweets were also unrealistic. Making Tesla private would cost roughly eighty billion dollars, including Tesla's debt. While he ultimately did not make Tesla private, he was sued by the Securities and Exchange Commission (SEC). In the SEC complaint, they claimed Musk's "funding secured" tweet was "false and misleading," as were his following tweets during the day. As a result, Musk's tweet caused "significant confusion and disruption in the market for Tesla's stock and

---

219 Sean O'Kane, "The message from Elon Musk's 'funding secured' mess is to never tweet," *The Verge*, August 7, 2019.

220 Ibid.

resulting harm to investors." His tweets also caused outrage from both technology and financial columnists in the media.[221]

One month later, Musk told Buzzfeed News Unsworth had moved to Thailand to take a child bride.[222] Two days later, Musk smoked marijuana on comedian Joe Rogan's popular podcast. With all of these negative incidents happening within the span of just one month, two of Tesla's top executives resigned the day after the podcast. Tesla's share prices fell to almost its lowest point of the year. There was concern about Musk's leadership ability and even calls for him to resign as CEO of Tesla and SpaceX.[223]

Musk attempted to rebuild Tesla's image by debuting their plan for their fully autonomous line of vehicles at an event called Autonomy Day on April 22, 2019. At this event, Musk said Tesla would have one million completely autonomous "robotaxis" on US roads by 2020. Musk also stated Tesla owners could make as much as thirty thousand dollars per year if they designated their car be used as a "robotaxi" when they weren't using them.[224]

As far back as 2016, he stated Tesla would be producing autonomous vehicles. He also said there would be a completely hands-free cross-country drive by a Tesla autonomous

---

221 Umair Irfan, "Elon Musk's tweet about taking Tesla private has triggered a federal lawsuit," *Vox*, September 28, 2018.

222 Ryan Mac, Mark Di Stefano, and John Paczkowski, "In a New Email, Elon Musk Accused a Cave Rescuer of Being a 'Child Rapist' and Says He 'Hopes' There's a Lawsuit," *BuzzFeed News*, September 4, 2018.

223 Emily Stewart, "Elon Musk's week of pot smoking and wild emails, explained," massive, September 8, 2018.

224 Todd Lassa, "Tesla Promises Full Level 5 by End of 2019, Model 3 Robotaxis by 2020," *Automobile*, April 23, 2019.

vehicle in 2017. Neither of these predictions proved to be true.[225]

I discussed the possibility of autonomous vehicle companies forming fleets of "robotaxis" as an initial commercial deployment with a graduate student and friend in Beijing. He said for Tesla, "The FSD (fully self-driving) service will be a subscription service like Netflix. You pay a certain fee every year, or every month, and the function will just work for you." He stated this approach makes sense for Tesla because it owns the entire technology stack, including the vehicles themselves. However, a variation of this model could also be used for technology companies like Baidu and Waymo. He said, "We (technology companies) can just rent it out to other companies and say, 'You can use it to make as many cars as you want, but you have to pay us X amount every month for using the data, algorithms, stuff like that.'" Therefore, Musk was trying to create an alternative business model to offset the increased cost of the vehicles themselves.

In an email to Tesla employees, Musk proclaimed Autonomous Day was "a great day for Tesla! The Autonomy Day was extremely well-received."[226]

However, many tech columnists remained skeptical. According to a CNBC article, published one day after the event, Musk "presented bold, visionary promises that only his most loyal followers would take at face value." Specifically, they pointed out perfecting the technology for Tesla vehicles to drive fully autonomously within one year was very unrealistic. Due to falling production of Tesla vehicles, the goal

225 Ibid.

226 Lora Kolodny, "Elon Musk sent a two-line email telling employees how great Tesla's autonomy day was, but it has lots of holes," *CNBC*, April 23, 2019.

of manufacturing one million vehicles was questionable as well. Finally, the salary earned by a driver from a ride-hailing app, such as Uber or Lyft, is too low for the expected money Tesla owner could expect to receive from converting their vehicle into a "robotaxi."[227]

MUSK NEEDS TO LET HIS ACHIEVEMENTS DO THE TALKING

While most of his predictions have been wrong, he was able to make one correct prediction. Back in 2018, Musk declared he would make one million electric cars by 2020. On March 10, 2020, Musk posted a tweet, saying, "Congratulations Tesla team on making our 1,000,000th car!!" Along with the tweet, he posted two photos. One photo was of the car itself, a shiny, red Tesla electric crossover vehicle. The other photo was of the entire Freemont, California team where the car was built.[228]

Elon Musk has incredible vision for new trends and markets to pursue. This vision was evident with his first ventures as an internet entrepreneur. He then changed paths completely, spending all of his money on two risky ventures with Tesla and SpaceX. Because of his leadership, he has made Tesla one of the most popular vehicle brands in the US and one of the premier electric vehicle companies in the world. He has also laid the foundation for the autonomous vehicle industry's success with the popular semi-autonomous Autopilot feature on his Tesla vehicles and creating an OTA system for downloading updates for these vehicles wirelessly.

All he has to do is make the media less of a villain and more of an advocate. Most of his missteps in this regard are

---

227 Ibid.

228 Jon Porter, "Tesla just made its one millionth car," *The Verge*, March 10, 2020.

self-inflicted. The vehicles he has created, his investment in things like charging infrastructure, the successful launches of goods, and now people in his rockets at SpaceX should do the talking for him. He's the one person in the autonomous vehicle industry in the US who draws enough attention to make autonomous vehicles as trusted and accepted as he's done with electric vehicles…if he chooses to do so.

The next section analyzes Xi Jinping's efforts to transform the Chinese economy. To do so, he must create ambitious new programs to make China a global leader in the production of new technology, such as the Made in China 2025 program. He must also manage the tension that this program creates with the US. The section also describes two Chinese companies, Baidu and startup AutoX, as they work to produce autonomous vehicles.

PART 3:

MAJOR PLAYERS IN CHINA

CHAPTER 9

THE DRAGON AWAKENS: XI JINPING LAYS THE PATH FOR CHINESE AUTONOMOUS VEHICLES

THE DRAGON STIRS AS XI JINPING TAKES POWER PROMISING A CHINA DREAM

"Generally speaking, the foundation of our scientific and technological innovation is not solid enough. Our independent innovation ability, especially in the area of original creativity, is not strong. We cannot always decorate our tomorrows with others' yesterdays. We cannot afford to lag behind in this important race. We must catch up and surpass others."[229]

GENERAL SECRETARY XI JINPING, *THE GOVERNANCE OF CHINA*

---

229 Elizabeth C. Economy, *The Third Revolution: Xi Jinping and the New Chinese State* (New York: Oxford University Press, 2018), 123.

* * *

This quote by General Secretary Xi Jinping expresses his frustration at China's lack of scientific and technological innovations. The quote also expresses Xi's desire to address this weakness. He would not be following old models, such as Deng Xiaoping's "Reform and Opening Up," but would be charting a new course. There would be new policies brought on by new ideas.

The quote also has global implications by framing this need to develop new technology as a race against "others" that China must catch up to and surpass. These "others" refer primarily to the US. Xi taking over as the leader of China marked the beginning of China's entry into the competition for global technological supremacy. The race to develop autonomous vehicles began. However, Xi first had to solidify his power at the top of the CCP hierarchy before he could create these new policies to revitalize China's slumbering technology sector.

Xi Jinping took over as General Secretary of the CCP and chairman of the Central Military Commission on November 15, 2012.[230] After he assumed power, Xi gave speeches about the China Dream. The China Dream has heavy Nationalist overtones of reasserting China's dominance in East Asia and around the world.[231] To accomplish such a lofty agenda, Xi would need to make new policies and changes to China's governance system.

---

230 John Ruwitch, "Timeline – The rise of Chinese leader Xi Jinping," *Reuters*, March 16, 2018.

231 Damian Grammaticas, "Chinese New President Xi Jinping: A man with a dream," *BBC* News, March 14, 2013.

Xi Jinping called innovation China's "Achille's heel," and forced it to take center stage.[232] To this end, Xi announced a huge new investment plan to develop China's tech sector called the Made in China 2025 program in May 2015.[233]

Xi also announced huge infrastructure and energy development loan programs all over the world soon after he took office in 2013. This policy was called the Belt and Road Initiative (BRI).[234]

Finally, Xi directed local leaders to create "New Infrastructure" projects like 5G networks and other infrastructure to support these new technology products. He also told them to focus on creating new high-tech products and services instead of the previous instructions to simply make money and advance China's economy.[235]

This was significant because, with this decision, Xi Jinping changed the incentive system for party leader advancement that had been in place since Deng Xiaoping announced his "Reform and Opening Up" policy in December 1978. The days of Deng's China "biding our time" was over. It was time to make the China Dream a reality.[236]

The Chinese economy needed to change. Because of the success of Deng's "Reform and Opening Up," Chinese people were no longer stuck in poverty. As a result of this,

---

232 Ben Blanchard, "Lack of innovation is 'Achilles heel' for Chinese economy, Xi says," *Reuters*, May 15, 2019.

233 Elsa B. Kania, "Made in China 2025, Explained," *The Diplomat*, February 1, 2019.

234 Suisheng Zhao, "The Belt and Road Initiative and Xi Jinping's foreign and domestic policy agenda," *The Asia Dialogue*, October 29, 2019.

235 James McBride and Andrew Chatzky, "Is 'Made in China 2025' a Threat to Global Trade?," *Council on Foreign Relations*, May 13, 2019.

236 Mark Preen, "Economic Reform in China: Current Progress and Future Prospects," *China Briefing*, April 3, 2019.

their wages had grown. The new middle class meant foreign countries were going elsewhere to manufacture their products more cheaply. The ways in which the Chinese economy would change was clear by looking at Xi's frustration with China's tech sector. He wanted to make China a new technology power, and he had global ambitions.

Xi Jinping mentioned China cannot simply follow the rules created by past leaders like Deng Xiaoping. However, the system created by Deng of central policies enacted by local leaders was so engrained in the system that it could not be entirely excised. Xi would need to first use his political cunning to surround himself with allies at the top of the CCP's governing apparatus. Once he could ensure his goals were presented as clearly as possible, he could establish the incentive structure which would ensure the local leaders followed his orders.

I interviewed my business consultant friend who works with "New Infrastructure" company clients in Beijing. He clarified the problem of enforcing the leader's goals nationwide: "Wherever they (autonomous vehicle companies) go, whether it's a city or province, they want them to be their test ground." This becomes difficult from the government's perspective "because of these two needs and incentives, you can see all kinds of corruption and grey areas going on." Therefore, Xi Jinping would first need to address the problem of corruption.

In this chapter, I will be discussing each of Xi Jinping's objectives to transform the Chinese economy. These political changes are important because they form the basis of China's technology sector. China's autonomous vehicle industry, and the financiers who support it, are tech companies. Describing its development under Xi Jinping is crucial to explain the development of China's autonomous vehicle industry.

XI JINPING LAUNCHES A WAR ON CORRUPTION AND WORKS TO CENTRALIZE POWER

Immediately after taking office as the General Secretary following the conclusion of the opening ceremony at the 18th National Congress of the CCP on November 8, 2012, Xi Jinping launched an anti-corruption campaign. There have been many anti-corruption campaigns throughout the history of the CCP, but they typically last only a few months or years and rarely target high-level officials. Xi declared this campaign would target and prosecute both "tigers and flies." "Tigers" refers to high-raking officials while "flies" meant low-level party cadres.[237]

Beyond the need to root out corrupt officials in the CCP, there were also political motives for Xi's arrests. He wanted to weed out any people disloyal to his rule. This would allow him to surround himself with loyalists for his ambitious agendas.[238]

Zhou Yongkang, mentor to Xi's political rival Bo Xilai, was one of the most powerful figures in the CCP. He served on the 17th Politburo Standing Committee (PSC) from 2007 to 2012 before he retired.[239] The PSC is a cabinet of seven top ministers who advise the General Secretary on key issues concerning policies for China's domestic and foreign policy.

---

237 Tania Branigan, "Xi Jinping vows to fight 'tigers' and 'flies' in anti-corruption drive," *The Guardian*, January 22, 2013.

238 Alexandra Fiol-Mahon, "Xi Jinping's Anti-Corruption Campaign: The Hidden Motives of a Modern Day Mao," *Foreign Policy Research Institute*, August 17, 2018.

239 Yuwen Wu, "Profile: China's fallen security chief Zhou Yongkang," *BBC* News, October 12, 2015.

Normally high-ranking officials have immunity from corruption investigations. However, the arrest of Bo before Xi officially took power gave warning to all CCP members that any perceived disloyalty to Xi would not be tolerated.[240]

In an effort to centralize power, Xi Jinping installed people loyal to him in the elite twenty-five-member Politburo and the PSC.[241] Xi also announced his desire to remove the term limits of the General Secretary position.[242] This move frightened Western analysts and policymakers following Xi's eventful early actions to combat corruption and proclaim a more aggressive Chinese foreign policy to advance its interests in the China Dream.

The Chinese People's Congress followed Xi's orders, passing an amendment to the CCP Constitution on March 11, 2018. This amendment removed the term limits.[243] Now Xi could serve as General Secretary for the rest of his life.

After ensuring his political stability, Xi Jinping focused on earning the trust and loyalty of the Chinese people. The "Xi Jinping Thought on Socialism with Chinese Characteristics for a New Era," or Xi Jinping Thought, has also been added to the Constitution. Interest in Xi Jinping thought spread throughout China. Local governments, scholars, universities, and businesses all made studying it a top priority to gain Xi's favor and demonstrate their loyalty.[244]

---

240 Andrei Lungu, "Interpreting the party's anti-corruption campaign," *RISAP*, September 27, 2017.

241 Chong Koh Ping, "China's Xi Jinping stacks 25-member Politburo with loyalists," *Straits Times*, October 25, 2017.

242 James Doubek, "China Removes Presidential Term Limits, Enabling Xi Jinping to Rule Indefinitely," NPR, March 11, 2018.

243 Ibid.

244 Kevin Carrico, "I Mastered Xi Jinping Thought and I Have the Certificate to Prove It," *Foreign Policy*, October 18, 2018.

Xi Jinping did not only want to focus on gaining the respect and adoration of the masses within China. Part of the China Dream is exerting greater influence on the world stage. One of the best ways to do so would be to start setting the global standards for new technology, such as autonomous vehicles.

I had a conversation with Michael Dunne, author of *American Wheels, Chinese Roads: The Story of General Motors in China*. I asked him whether setting the global standards for autonomous vehicles would be important. He replied, "Yes, China wants not only to create and set the standards but also to extend those standards into other markets...probably not the US. But you could see them getting tighter with Europe and of course places like Southeast Asia, African and South America and saying we're the new standard of the world." He continued to say this would be shocking for US business leaders, who have grown accustomed to being the global standard setters for decades.

Mr. Dunne then said it would be hard for many in the US business community to imagine not having the leverage that comes with authoring standards. There is an increased attention paid by Xi to creating new global standards. The absence, or lack of interest in engagement, of the US in some of these governing institutions, like the UN, creates a potential change in how standards are set.

Setting the global standards for safety for autonomous vehicles would be significant in deciding who "wins" the race. An important point to setting these standards would be to first assure the technology's success in China. How would this new emphasis on developing technological innovations work in practice? Or would this just be another empty slogan?

MADE IN CHINA 2025 MORE THAN JUST A SLOGAN?

Many different opinions exist about the massive economic restructuring effort currently underway in China. Some scholars are broadly skeptical this push by Xi will not be successful. One of these skeptics is Dr. Elizabeth Economy, who wrote a book on this subject called *The Third Revolution: Xi Jinping and the New Chinese State.*

In this book, Dr. Economy argues Xi Jinping is leading a third revolution of the socio-political and economic order in China. She argues, for instance, Xi's emphasis on innovation has led to patents for improvements on existing technologies but there is not a lot of new truly innovative goods or services.[245]

She does describe the great work done by new tech start-ups and new tech incubators, such as the one run by Lee Kai-fu. However, she finds many problems in her section describing the Chinee government's efforts to develop the electric vehicle industry. This was one of the first efforts by China to push for the development of new technology on a large scale in the last ten years.

Dr. Economy describes how Xi seeks to accomplish the goal of not following the example of other leaders of China in his innovation paths for the future. According to Xi, China must spend on talent, spend on infrastructure, spend on research and development, and spend on other's research.[246]

The effort to create an electric vehicle (EV) industry actually started before Xi took office, with his predecessor Hu Jintao.[247] I will not focus on an in-depth analysis of the EV

---

245 Elizabeth C. Economy, *The Third Revolution: Xi Jinping and the New Chinese State* (New York: Oxford University Press, 2018), 125.

246 Ibid. 123

247 Ibid. 127

industry development like Dr. Economy. I will instead focus on a few key pieces which she discusses related to the political decisions made by the CCP in their push to support this new technology.

I will then discuss the possible similarities and differences this investment in EV development has for China's "New Infrastructure" development projects. These "New Infrastructure" projects are important because they have direct implications for the successful integration of autonomous vehicles into China's existing transit system.

In Dr. Economy's chapter on innovation, "Innovation Nation," she describes China's definition of innovation as not advancing frontiers, but as being process driven, i.e. to make existing products better or faster. Essentially it is innovation based on commercialization and making products to meet the needs of consumers.[248]

Xi Jinping continued Hu Jintao's policy to develop China's EV industry, even though it had failed to excel under Hu because he saw an opening in the electric vehicle market. Producing EVs could establish China as a global leader in the field. It could also fill a consumer demand for vehicles by China's growing middle class. Finally, it could reduce the harmful air pollution in Chinese cities caused by carbon dioxide emissions from vehicle exhaust.[249]

In 2010, a plan was introduced by the CCP that stated ten cities would produce at least one thousand EVs by 2015.[250] Each city could set its own standards and technology. One year later, the list of cities expanded to twenty-five. [251] The

---

248 Ibid. 122

249 Ibid. 126

250 Ibid. 127-128

251 Ibid. 128

government gave massive subsidies to primarily State-Owned Enterprises (SOEs.) Anyone who purchased an EV made by a Chinese company would receive between fifty to sixty thousand RMB (roughly eleven thousand dollars at the time).[252]

The main problems Dr. Economy addressed were massive subsidies to SOEs and local governments. There was also little regulation related to how the money was spent or standards for the vehicles produced.[253] Another problem was the exclusion of foreign companies from effectively competing with Chinese companies. This lack of a viable competition led to a lack of incentive to improve the quality of their EVs.[254]

Xi continued to pursue the plan as it was originally conceived, at least for the first round from 2010 to 2015. This plan could potentially be a disaster. The huge subsidies, given to occasionally inefficient and corrupt SOEs, opened the door to mismanagement and fraud. This went directly against his popular anti-corruption campaign. Xi needed to direct his attention to solidifying his power in the CCP and could not devote it to this policy until after the first phase was complete in 2015.

The initial results of developing the EV industry was a failure. Only seven of the original ten cities reached the modest target of producing one thousand EVs. Rather than foster a healthy competition between Chinese EV companies, the massive subsidies created an over-saturation of EV companies. According to one count, Dr. Economy states there was only a total of 4,400 EVs sold from 2010 to 2015.[255]

---

252 Ibid. 128

253 Ibid. 127-128

254 Ibid. 128

255 Ibid. 128

Furthermore, there was a lack of coordination and planning between different EV companies and the electric grid. EVs purchased in one province could not be charged at a charging station in another province. There could be different vehicle designs, differences in the charging infrastructure, or both, in the two provinces.[256]

There was extensive fraud as well. Companies would inflate their production and sales figures. Some of their vehicles they did produce had no seats or sometimes even no battery. Sometimes a company would receive a subsidy and not develop any vehicles at all.[257] The result of this first five years was massive inefficiency, wasted resources, and billions of dollars lost in fraudulent activity.

The policy did improve after this initial period once Xi had solidified his power at the top of the CCP hierarchy. I had an interview with Zifei Yang, passenger vehicle program lead at the International Council on Clean Transportation (ICCT). She said, "China had some loopholes in the resolution in the beginning. After the exposure of the corruption and fraud, China significantly improved the policy design in terms of the incentives or subsidies in order to truly promote the advanced EV technologies."

Dr. Economy agreed with her because she noted in 2016 China fined five companies 225 million dollars for violating the subsidies and for reporting false vehicle sales figures.[258] The CCP established significantly stricter rules companies

256 Antony Ingram, "Has China 'Messe Up' Its Electric Car Charging Standards," *Green Car Reports*, July 24, 2014.

257 Nick Marro, Hengrui Liu, and Yu Yan, "Opportunities and Challenges in China's Electric Vehicle Market," *China Business Review*, February 2, 2015.

258 Hongyang Cui, "Subsidy fraud leads to reform for China's EV market," *ICCT*, May 30, 2017.

must follow in order to receive subsidies in 2017. They also said it would only give fifteen companies subsidies.[259]

Ms. Yang continued to say, "It is good China discovered the corruption and fraud at this stage so that it will get a chance to revise the policy design and do their best to close the policy loopholes." Regardless of whether you want to frame these problems as companies exploiting loopholes, like Ms. Yang, or failure to create helpful policies and relying on SOEs, like Dr. Economy, the results of these reforms were successful.

After the initial problems, China has been the world's leader in sales of plug-in electric vehicles since 2015. The auto market in China in general has seen a decrease in sales since mid 2018 because auto sales tend to work in cycles and China's rate of steady increases in sales was unsustainable long term. Other factors, such as the popularity and availability of public transportation and the ease and affordability of travelling by taxi, also played a role in this decline. The government has not relaxed its support for EVs, arguing it would like to see 25 percent of all vehicles in China be EVs by 2025.[260]

The EV industry's successful turnaround in China creates some cause for optimism for the autonomous vehicle industry but the EV industry's early failures present problems. A key difference in the early stages of these two industries' development is companies and major financiers in the autonomous vehicle industry are technology companies and not SOEs. The relatively small number of companies in the

---

259 Ilaria Mazzocco, "Electrifying: How China Built an EV Industry in a Decade," *Macro Polo*, July 8, 2020.

260 Yilei Sun and Brenda Goh, "China wants new energy vehicle sales in 2025 to be 25% of all car sale," *Reuters*, December 7, 2019.

autonomous vehicle industry also increases the competition with, hopefully, a corresponding increase in quality.

The autonomous vehicle industry itself is not a job creator. However, local leaders are now incentivized to create new high-tech products. Especially during the economic downturn, as a result of the COVID-19 pandemic, they must also provide different groups of people with jobs. The clearest parallel from the problems that plagued the EV industry in China to the autonomous vehicle industry would be the creation of "New Infrastructure" projects, which would also support autonomous vehicles. These projects would both employ a wide variety of people to fulfill both technical and manual labor tasks and comprise a mix of private companies and SOEs.

NEW INFRASTRUCTURE DEVELOPMENT: A CAUSE FOR CONCERN OR A MANAGEABLE SITUATION?

My business consultant friend working in Beijing explained there are four key infrastructure projects currently in development in China related to autonomous vehicles. The first is a 5G network, which I discussed the importance of in chapter two for Over-the-Air (OTA) data updates for autonomous vehicles and for receiving teleoperations assistance in case of an emergency. The 5G wireless network connection also allows autonomous vehicles to communicate to and receive communications from the other infrastructure installments in this system.

Roadside cameras or sensors are the second important piece. These cameras and sensors collect information about the traffic on the road from connected or autonomous vehicles. Cameras and sensors then send this data to another network, which would be the third infrastructure instalment in the system.

The third infrastructure device works in tandem with the cameras and sensors as a "platform network." This network analyzes the data received from the cameras and sensors and sends it to both the stoplights and back to the vehicles.[261] This allows for safer driving by the vehicles because they have a better idea of the traffic conditions. It also allows for improved management of the traffic conditions because the city now has more information to properly time the traffic lights in the stoplights.

The final piece of infrastructure does not need to be on or even near the road, but it is still critical. This infrastructure piece is a data center. Data centers are for data storage and processing. This piece is either owned by the autonomous vehicle companies or a third party who provides "infrastructure as a service."[262] It is used to store the huge amount of data collected by the vehicle for each ride and process this data. This allows the companies to have the data to develop the automated driving system.

My friend then said, "It (the infrastructure system) needs to be synchronized, it needs to be well-established, to have the right scale, and the coverage in order for autonomous driving to actually work." When I asked about how far China was in this process, he said, "All four of them are far away from being really applicable to society, at this point."

When I asked about how the policy is being developed, he revealed different cities want to be the "hub for self-driving cars" because of the structure of the incentive system to create more high-value goods and industries. Just being this

261 Michael Keller, "This is how road networks determine traffic capacity," *World Economic Forum*, November 22, 2019.

262 Zeus Kerravala, "What are data centers? How they work and how they are changing in size and scope," *Network World*, September 25, 2017.

hub is not enough. He revealed, "They want their factories, their research labs, they want to have the entire ecosystem of technology firms, AI companies, 5G companies, camera companies…Essentially, all of the leaders of these cities want their city to become the next Silicon Valley of China."

China currently lacks some of the necessary infrastructure projects and needs to build them in order to catch up to and potentially surpass the US. It is actually a good thing that cities are advocating and pushing for new technology and infrastructure. This would better enable autonomous vehicle companies to commercialize their vehicles when they are safe enough to do so. I detail two examples in this book of companies taking advantage of this effort to develop new technology and infrastructure in cities to secure benefits for their companies.

AutoX has an eighty-thousand-square-foot autonomous "robotaxi" center in Shanghai.[263] Baidu has also won bids from several cities to establish test facilities because of the incentives for the leaders of these city governments.[264]

China's push for new technology as part of the Made in China 2025 program and the related support structure in the "New Infrastructure" policy experienced some growing pains with the early stage of the EV industry. However, the Chinese government has learned from these early mistakes. Innovative technology companies have led the way in China's autonomous vehicle industry and have the support of local governments. These local governments are building the

263 Catherine Shu, "AutoX launches its Robo Taxi service in Shanghai, competing with Didi's pilot program," *TechCrunch*, August 17, 2020.

264 Sarah Dai, "Baidu to build self-driving test facility in Chongqing as the Chinese city pushes ahead with smart city infrastructure," *South China Morning Post*, March 20, 2020.

infrastructure and support systems required for autonomous vehicles to succeed.

This massive increase in government and corporation spending on "New Infrastructure" projects follows a pattern by the CCP of investment-driven growth during periods of economic downturn. It invested heavily in infrastructure projects (roads, rail lines, train stations, et cetera) during the Great Recession in 2009 through 2010, and again in 2015. Because of the economic impact of the COVID-19 pandemic, loss of factory production, and decline in both domestic and foreign demand for goods and services, China reported its GDP shrank by 6.9 percent in the first quarter of 2020.[265]

China invests in infrastructure because it has a multiplier effect of about three, the highest of any developed economy. This means a one dollar increase in real government spending can raise real GDP immediately by about three dollars. This would be a tool for China to reverse economic decline and recover from the economic impact of the pandemic more quickly than other countries. The investment-led growth has drawbacks. Notably among them is over-investment and over-production. This has led to the "ghost cities" in parts of China where the investment boom in 2009 and 2015 led to massive increases in apartment building complexes with a lack of actual occupants in these buildings. This can also lead to bad debt and nonperforming loans. This debt problem brought on by over-investment troubles economists analyzing China's financial system.[266]

Chinese "robotaxi" companies, chief among them AutoX and Didi (a ride-hailing company similar to Uber), and

---

265 Umesh Desai, "Huge investment in 'new infra' key to China's recovery," *Asia Times*, April 27, 2020.

266 Ibid.

several new ride-hailing and grocery delivery startups have benefitted from this investment. Leading companies in the US, such as Waymo, Chevy Cruise, Argo.ai, and Zoox, have halted or stopped testing passenger autonomous vehicles during the second quarter of 2020. That has not been the case with companies in China. According to a spokesperson from AutoX, "The pandemic has made people in China realize robotaxis and robo-delivery are much safer ways of transportation for people and goods. Safety does not only mean less traffic accidents but also less risk of contact and infection." Whether or not this trend continues after the pandemic has subsided remains to be seen, but this acceptance of autonomous vehicles is a welcome sign for companies in China.[267]

The more proactive public-private partnership between the government and technology companies, particularly the autonomous vehicle industry, paves the way for them to succeed in China. As I mentioned in the introduction to this chapter, Xi Jinping has global ambitions for developing the new technology produced in the Made in China 2025 program. The question to then ask is how will the Chinese government, and Chinese technology firms, respond to the pressure of competing with the US? Also, how will the escalating trade, economic, and security tensions between these two countries impact the autonomous vehicle industry, not just in China, but in the US? After all, the autonomous vehicle supply chain is global. A disruption with a trade dilemma between the two largest economies in the world will have global implications.

---

267 Larry Mullin, "China's cities will soon be crawling with self-driving robotaxis," *Fast Company*, September 24, 2020.

THE CHINA DREAM COULD BECOME A NIGHTMARE AS TRADE WAR TENSIONS HEAT UP

In China, beginning in elementary school and continuing throughout a person's life, they are taught about China's five thousand years of history. During the period of dynastic rule, China or 中国, the "Middle Kingdom," saw itself as the center of the universe. Representatives of other countries had to bow down before the emperor and offer goods as part of the "tributary system." In return, their countries were granted trading rights with China, their leaders received political recognition, and occasionally economic or military aid to defeat rival leaders.[268]

On November 15, 2012, Xi Jinping addressed the Great Hall of the People in Beijing. In his speech he mentioned China's five-thousand-year history, which had made an "indelible contribution" to global civilization. Xi then called for "the great revitalization of the Chinese nation" after others had "failed one time after another" in this goal.[269]

Xi's "great revitalization" refers to his China Dream. The policies he has pursued in pursuit of that dream include the BRI, Made in China 2025, and the push for "New Infrastructure" projects described in this chapter. Implicit in the speech is his criticism of his predecessors for not reaching these goals and the implication he would not fail as they had done.

US President Donald Trump has failed to respect Xi's passion for making China a respected world power, and Trump's anti-China rhetoric during and after the 2016 presidential

---

268 Eric Teo Chu Cheow, "Asian Security and the Reemergence of China's Tributary System," *The Jamestown Foundation*, September 16, 2004.

269 Elizabeth Economy, "History With Chinese Characteristics," *Foreign Affairs*, July/August 2017.

election campaign have resulted in faltering trade negotiations between these two countries.[270] This created misperceptions in China about the seriousness of trade negotiations on the part of the US. The resulting trade war between the two largest economies in the world could slow down Xi's great ambitions for the China Dream.

Another point of historical misunderstanding concerns the "Century of Humiliation." This concept refers to the century beginning with the Treaty of Nanking which ended the First Opium War between China and the United Kingdom. This treaty gave Hong Kong to the UK and opened several new trade ports for British merchants to sell goods to China with no restrictions. Similar treaties were signed in the 1850s by China, ruled by the Qing empire, with Russia, the US, and France.[271]

This "Century of Humiliation" is reinforced throughout a person's life in China as much as the pride of its five-thousand-year history. China will always approach any trade negotiation with wariness and skepticism, particularly negotiations involving the US. Cutting subsidies to its SOEs, getting rid of the technology transfer requirements, and opening the country to allow for the import of more goods would be difficult for China to accept.

However, the main issue of contention from the Chinese side involves the measures demanded by the US for enforcement of any Chinese companies who do not live up the terms of the agreement.[272]

---

270 Veronica Stracqualursi, "10 times Trump attacked China and its trade relations with the U.S.," *ABC News*, November 9, 2017.

271 Alan Rappeport, "19th-Century 'Humiliation' Haunts China-US Trade Talks," *The New York Times*, March 27, 2019.

272 Ibid.

One US Senator involved in the trade negotiation strategy described what he viewed as the proper enforcement mechanism. "What we want is the ability to put on unilateral tariffs that can't be counteracted by a tariff from China," Senator Charles E. Grassley of Iowa, the Republican chairman of the Senate Finance Committee, told reporters.[273]

The desire by US policymakers to assure China abides by a deal is justified because there is a lack of transparency and inflated sales figures inherent in China's public-private partnership. This was evident in the fraud uncovered by companies in the EV industry, as described above. However, this strategy by the US indicates a failure to understand Chinese history and echoes the unfair treaties signed by China during the "Century of Humiliation." Any request for "unilateral tariffs" would immediately raise red flags for any Chinese negotiator, given how engrained this troubling history is for everyone in China. Negotiators from China and the US should have knowledge of both the issues that could cause negotiations to fail and each side's intentions behind their demands to reach a deal suitable for both countries.

Both the US and China have underestimated the other country's resolve and have overestimated their own leverage at different times during this trade dispute. However, it is in neither country's interest to prolong this trade war, particularly for their country's respective autonomous vehicle industries. Trade conflict between China and the US creates a lose-lose situation for companies in both countries.

The push for electric vehicles he inherited from his predecessor showed the growing pains of Xi's effort to revitalize China's economy with Made in China 2025. Xi turned

---

273 Ibid.

this failure into a success through policy revisions. China now produces more electric vehicles than any country in the world. China's investment in "New Infrastructure" projects supports the investment in new technology, particularly autonomous vehicles. This bodes well for the future of the autonomous vehicle industry in China.

CHAPTER 10

US-CHINA TRADE AND SECURITY TENSION COULD TURN THE CHINA DREAM TO A NIGHTMARE

PAYING FOR A TAXI, HAIRCUT, OR YOUR HOME ELECTRICITY BILL? THERE'S AN APP FOR THAT

"Twenty-four people went for that job. Twenty-three were accepted. I was the one guy who was not," Jack Ma said after applying for a job at KFC after he graduated from college.[274] In 1999, Ma returned to his hometown of Hangzhou with a team of people to found Alibaba, a business-to-business marketplace.[275]

---

274 Charlie Rose, "Charlie Rose Talks to Alibaba's Jack Ma," *Bloomberg Businessweek*, January 29, 2015.

275 Stevan Popovic, "Jack Ma: The man leading the Chinese e-commerce market," *Hot Topics*, May 4, 2014.

In September 2014, Alibaba raised over twenty-five billion dollars in its Initial Public Offering (IPO) on the New York Stock Exchange.[276] This was the largest IPO in the Stock Exchange's financial history, and Ma is now one of the richest people in the world.

Like many figures in the Chinese technology and autonomous vehicle industry, Ma represents a true rags-to-riches story. He grew up in Hangzhou and learned English by talking to English-speaking foreigners at Hangzhou International Hotel. He also rode his bicycle seventeen miles every day to give tourists tours of the area for free in order to continue to practice his English.[277]

However, he soon met with a series of disappointments. Chinese high school students take one test, the 高考 (Big Test). This test determines which university they will attend, or even whether they qualify to attend a university at all. Ma failed the test two times before he finally passed it and attended Hangzhou Teacher's Institute. This university is now Hangzhou Normal University. He graduated in 1988 with a BA in English.[278]

Ma's next difficulties came when he applied for jobs after he graduated. He applied for thirty jobs, including one at KFC, and no one hired him.[279] He also applied to Harvard Business School ten times and was rejected each time.[280]

---

276 Elzko Barreto, "Alibaba IPO Is Officially the Biggest Ever at $25 Billion," *Business Insider*, September 22, 2014.

277 Leelian Kong, "What Jack Ma can teach international students about learning English," *Study International News*, June 25, 2018.

278 Charlie Rose, "Charlie Rose Talks to Alibaba's Jack Ma," *Bloomberg Businessweek*, January 29, 2015.

279 Ibid.

280 Jack Ma, "Jack Ma: 'Harvard rejected me 10 times,'" *World Economic Forum*, September 14, 2015.

Ma travelled to the US for the first time in 1995 and was exposed to the internet for the first time. When he returned to China, he built his first what he called "ugly" website simply named "The Internet."[281]

One of the keys to Alibaba's success was Jack Ma's decision to create an app called Alipay. This app, under Alibaba's financial company Ant Financial, gave consumers a fast and secure way to pay for goods and services for the Alibaba startup Taobao.[282]

I interviewed Chris Miller from the US-China Business Council's Shanghai office and asked him about the importance of Alipay for the Chinese technology sector. He said, "Well, when the company was in its early years, Alibaba wanted people to make online purchases, but there was a lack of trust in payment security." He said, "Whether that meant exposure of bank card data (to other people) or trust that merchants would actually send goods following payment (which wasn't always the case at the time)."

He continued, referencing the risk of making purchases online in China, saying, "Without escrow, scams can become a serious problem. The best way to solve this was to come up with our own payment system, so they pioneered a secure way of facilitating that." He concluded by saying, "Although it is now ubiquitous due to other factors, security has been a core from day one." Essentially, they created Alipay because they had no other choice if they wanted people to trust their payments would be safe and secure.

---

281 Helen H. Wang, "Alibaba Sage III: Jack Ma Discovered the Internet," *Forbes*, July 17, 2014.

282 Zen Soo and Li Tao, "How Alibaba's Taobao solved the trust problem in China and changed the way people shop," *South China Morning Post*, August 24, 2018.

Today, everything can be purchased or sold using Alipay or the similar app, WeChat Pay. This app is from popular Chinese social media app WeChat. It can be used to pay for a wide variety of goods and services, from coffee at a local Starbucks, to a soda from a vending machine, to taxi fare, and even a person's gas or electric bill.[283] This has opened the door to businesses in all fields to sell goods and services directly to consumers.

Mobile payment can also be used by autonomous vehicle companies to create an easy way for passengers to pay their taxi fares in an autonomous "robotaxi." AutoX, mentioned in the last chapter with their new "robotaxi" base in Shanghai, has Alibaba as one of its main financial backers.[284] Therefore they have a proven, successful model, and support from Alibaba, in their effort to create a mobile app for passengers to pay their taxi fares.

This chapter analyzes the controversy which has emerged over China's mobile payment system. This system could represent a new financial framework for countries, but questions arise about governments tracking people's purchase history. The chapter also discusses the revolutionary benefits of 5G technology, as well as the controversy it generates. As China attempts to export this technology to the US and its allies, it has caused controversy because of security concerns related to espionage. China's efforts to work toward technological self-sufficiency in response to the trade dilemma show China's weakness in some technologies. This weakness could cause delays in China's efforts to achieve Xi's China Dream.

---

283 Ibid.

284 Kelly Earley, "AutoX raises $100m from Dongfeng Motor and Alibaba," *Silicon Republic*, September 17, 2019.

CONTROVERSY EMERGES FOR THIS INNOVATIVE PAYMENT METHOD

Mobile payment systems, such as Alipay and WeChat Pay, have existed largely without government regulation and control. However, this has changed in recent years. The lack of regulation was probably due to the fact it was initially a relatively insignificant part of the Chinese economy.[285]

However, in 2016 China saw nine trillion dollars in mobile payments. This dwarfs the one hundred twelve billion dollars of mobile payments in the US. The People's Bank of China (PBOC) implemented a new regulatory provision on June 30, 2018 which stated the government must clear all mobile payments through the PBOC.[286]

These mobile payment systems represent an alternative method for countries seeking to escape the credit system dominated by the West, particularly the US. The mobile payment system also raises concerns for human rights advocates for its potential role in creating the "social credit system" in China.[287]

Monitoring a person's purchases is not unique to China. For example, having a poor credit score in the US could prevent a person from getting a mortgage on a house, or applying for a loan to start a business.

What could be potentially worrying is how the Chinese government has adopted the QR code payment system as an identification system to monitor its citizens' payment history. The video cameras described in the last chapter are not just

---

285 Andrew Liu, "An Analysis of the PBOC's New Mobile Payment Regulation," *Winter 2019 Cato Journal*, 2019.

286 Ibid.

287 Nick Frisch, "We Should Worry About How China Uses Apps Like TikTok," *The New York Times*, May 2, 2019.

for tracking traffic trends. Millions of cameras are in cities all over China. These cameras are equipped with facial recognition technology to monitor even petty infractions like jaywalking.[288] While the mobile payment system makes it easier for customers to pay for items, it also gives the government a much easier way to fine people.

Scanning QR codes for mobile payment apps has its advantages for monitoring people during the current COVID-19 pandemic. This would give the government information about people's location and what they were spending their money on. This would allow for things like contact tracing to avoid spreading the coronavirus.[289]

Alipay and WeChat Pay cannot be entirely to blame for this perceived government invasion into people's privacy. They had no intention of using QR codes as an identification tool to track people's spending history.

My business consultant friend in Beijing described the effect it has on his daily life. He divulged, "Wherever you go, you have to scan a QR code...whether you're going to your apartment, your office building, and a shopping mall, et cetera." He continued to describe how this is impacting tech firms in China. He said, "I think for tech firms, it's never been a good time, especially if your business model is directly connecting to consumers."

He pointed out that the online gaming industry is doing very well and Tencent has experienced record stock increases for its online gaming platforms. However, autonomous

---

288 Chris Baynes, "Chinese police to use facial recognition technology to send jaywalkers instant fines by text," *Independent*, March 29, 2018.

289 Yan Xiao, "How digital payments can help countries cope with COVID-19, other pandemics: Lessons from China," *World Economic Forum*, May 6, 2020.

vehicles would clearly fall into the category of a technology which directly connects to consumers. There could be a slower start to the "robotaxi" fleet services in China. This is true even with favorable regulations because of the pandemic.

With its mobile payment system, China makes it easier for companies to start and run businesses with a secure and easy way to buy and sell products and services. This system also provides an alternative to the US credit system. Human rights organizations have cause for concern about the spread of this technology. China's push for another revolutionary technology with 5G could be a substantial benefit to their technology sector. However, this technology has become a central piece of the trade conflict between China and the US because of fears of CCP espionage.

CHINA SEEKS TO LEAD THE WORLD IN 5G TECHNOLOGY

Huawei Technology's founder and CEO Ren Zhengfei, a former engineer in the People's Liberation Army (PLA), requires employees to have military discipline and toughness. Before new employees start working at Huawei's headquarters in Shenzhen, they must travel to the company's training facility called Huawei University.[290]

At the site, new employees must undergo a two-week-long boot camp. Everyone sleeps in dormitories and wakes up at 5 a.m. for running and other exercises in Huawei uniforms. They then attend classes literally called "brainwashing." These classes cover history, Huawei company products,

290 Anna Fifield, "'Bloodthirsty' like a wolf: Inside the military-style discipline at China's tech titan, Huawei," *The Washington Post*, December 13, 2018.

and discuss the company's work culture. This culture was described as "bloodthirsty like a wolf" by an employee.[291]

These business camps are not uncommon in China. However, Huawei's work culture sets it apart from other companies. A former employee, speaking anonymously, called his first year at Huawei "panful," but he later said, "If it wasn't because of the passion, if it wasn't because of the striving, how could Huawei be where it is today?"[292]

The passion of CEO Ren Zhengfei has led Huawei to become one of the biggest tech companies in China. It has also led Huawei to lead China's push for global 5G dominance. This push has also earned Huawei the ire of US President Donald Trump.

5G networks allow users and products, such as autonomous vehicles, Virtual Reality (VR) headsets, and other artificial intelligence products, to download data wirelessly at blazing fast speeds. 5G is significantly more capable than the current top-speed 4G-LTE wireless networks in the US.

According to Qualcomm's official site, it is roughly ten times faster than 4G-LTE, with a peak downloading speed of twenty gigabits per second (GBps). It also has over one hundred megabits per second (MBps) average data rate. This increased speed would allow a person to download a movie in seconds.[293]

There is also significantly lower latency with 5G. This reduced latency allows it to deliver more instantaneous, real-time data transfer of one millisecond. This would reduce

---

291 Ibid.

292 Ibid.

293 "Everything you need to know about 5G," Research & Invention, *Qualcomm*, last modified 2020.

the lag time for devices such as video games and make VR headsets run much more smoothly.[294]

Finally, 5G networks offer more capacity. This means more people can use it at once because it is designed to support a one hundred-times increase in traffic capacity and network efficiency. Therefore, more people could effectively stream on more devices in a household.[295]

I discussed the benefits of a 5G network connection for autonomous vehicles in my chapter introducing the near-term use cases of autonomous vehicles to the US. These benefits include the ability to rapidly download large and frequent data updates wirelessly to the autonomous vehicle. These updates could include map updates to the vehicle's cloud computing system or other perception updates. 5G network connections would also allow for remote operators to more easily recognize a problem and assist people driving an autonomous vehicle to prevent an accident.

Huawei and SOE ZTE have created 5G network connections in cities all over China. As discussed in the last chapter, the 5G network connectivity assists autonomous vehicles to communicate with both other vehicles and roadside infrastructure crucial to the success of autonomous vehicles. However, Xi Jinping and the CCP's efforts to export this technology cause concerns related to the security of these networks. US policymakers fear the CCP could create a backdoor in the network to spy on corporations and foreign governments.

---

294 Ibid.

295 Ibid.

HUAWEI AND SOE ZTE GO GLOBAL LEADING TO RETALIATION BY THE US

Huawei and ZTE have invested heavily in 5G equipment in China and have also begun to export their 5G equipment. At the first Belt and Road Initiative Forum in May 2017, Xi Jinping proclaimed China would integrate big data into the BRI. The BRI consists of loans to developing countries in Asia, Europe, South America, and Africa.[296]

By including the development of a 5G network in this plan, Xi Jinping intends to create "the digital Silk Road of the 21st Century." Emphasizing 5G expansion has raised alarms in the US because ZTE is a State-Owned Enterprise (SOE) and there are suspicions Huawei is too close to the CCP. Zhengfei categorically denies this assertion, but Huawei's support for the CCP on projects such as the BRI raise serious questions about Ren's denials of CCP interference.[297]

Zhengfei is notoriously private and has rarely spoken to the media since he founded the company back in 1987. Ren's daughter and Huawei CFO Meng Wanzhou was arrested in Canada in December 2018 on orders from President Trump. She was then extradited to the US on charges of bank and wire fraud in violation of America's sanctions against Iran.[298] Meng's arrest came during trade negotiations between China and the US and was one of the reasons why the negotiations failed.

---

296 Shannon Tiezzi, "What did China Accomplish at the Belt and Road Forum?," *The Diplomat*, May 16, 2017.

297 "Huawei founder Ren Zhengfei denies firm poses spying risk," *BBC News*, January 15, 2019.

298 Amanda Coletta, "Canadian court rules extradition case against Huawei executive Meng Wanzhou can proceed," *The Washington Post*, May 27, 2020.

The US and China almost came to a trade agreement in April 2019. President Trump even started planning for a signing ceremony. However, there was less enthusiasm by China and they decided not to sign it.[299]

Largely seen as retaliation for the failure to come to a deal with China, Trump signed an executive order the following month banning Huawei equipment in the US. This was followed almost immediately by numerous government agencies also banning Huawei products and services. These agencies have created export controls of equipment to Huawei for their products.[300]

The decision by President Trump to arrest Wanzhou and ban Huawei has led to widespread anger by the people in China. The US is seen as going after one of China's greatest success stories. These actions recall the painful memories of China's traumatic "Century of Humiliation" from the nineteenth century of a foreign country attacking Chinese companies unjustly.

Zhengfei has downplayed questions of rivalry with the US. He said technology companies have a "peaceful competition."[301] This may be true for the companies themselves. However, these companies do not compete in a vacuum. Zhengfei ignores Xi Jinping's effort to transform the Chinese economy and the geo-political battle for technological and political supremacy between the US and China.

---

299 Jenny Leonard, Enda Curran, and Bloomberg, "How the US-China Trade war Has Reached a Turning Point," *Fortune*, April 17, 2019.

300 Sean Keane, "Huawei ban timeline: India will reportedly phase Huawei gear out as border tensions rise," *cnet*, August 25, 2020.

301 "Exclusive interview of Huawei founder Ren Zhengfei: Technology competition is peaceful game," *CGTN*, January 21, 2019.

Like it or not, Zhengfei's calls for peace often fall on deaf ears in Washington, DC. President Trump does not see the competition as peaceful. He sees it as a challenge to the US's global technological supremacy and leadership. This gives Xi Jinping the potential to advocate for standards that advance his interests over the interests of the US.

The US has not been able to offer a viable alternative for 5G technology. Large US carriers like Sprint and Verizon offer expanded 5G access to consumers. However, they lack the critical wireless infrastructure to access 5G network connections. The US needs to import this technology from Sweden's Ericsson or Finland's Nokia.[302]

The US has a weakness and vulnerability for the infrastructure which allows for 5G networks. China has two companies, Huawei and ZTE, to provide 5G connections to support all of its new technology products, including autonomous vehicles. China's weak semiconductor industry for fabricating critical computer microchips could slow Xi's plans for the China Dream, especially if trade tensions with the US continue.

CRACKS IN CHINA'S ARMOR: HOW BEING LATE IN THE SEMICONDUCTOR INDUSTRY COULD SLOW CHINA'S AUTONOMOUS VEHICLE INDUSTRY

Chinese companies have made enormous progress in advancing new technological developments in recent years. According to the World Intellectual Property Organization, in 2019 Chinese companies narrowly beat companies from the US (58,990 to 57,830) in patent applications. This was the first

302 Arjun Kharpal, "Trump 'apoplectic' with U.K. over Huawei 5G decision as US suggests taking stake in Nokia, Ericsson," *CNBC*, February 7, 2020.

time the US did not file the most patents since the figures were recorded in 1978.[303]

This also represents a two-hundred-fold increase for China in the last twenty years.[304] Elizabeth Economy argues most of the patents are just improvements on existing products and not brand-new products that change industries. However, this is an impressive milestone to celebrate for Chinese companies and for Xi's Made in China 2025 program.

One flaw which could slow down China's ability to continue on this breakneck pace is their weak semiconductor industry. This industry is responsible for producing high-quality microchips for computers and computerized technology. These microchips are a critical component for the automate driving systems for autonomous vehicles.

Semiconductors, and the machines fabricating microchips, represent some of the most complex technology in the world. Very few countries and companies have mastered this technology. This is because it requires a group of highly skilled, expensive staff with years of training to even design the machines required to fabricate the microchips.[305] Autonomous vehicles in particular need extremely advanced and powerful microchips to produce the processing power necessary to drive a vehicle autonomously.

Because the microchip fabrication process is so complex, the supply chain for microchips is global. For the most

303 "China Becomes Top Filer of International Patents in 2019 Amid Robust Growth for WIPO's IP Services, Treaties and Finances," *WIPO*, April 7, 2020.

304 Ibid.

305 Josh Herwitz, "Why the semiconductor is suddenly at the heart of US-China tech tension," *Quartz*, July 24, 2018.

difficult to fabricate microchips, like CPUs and GPUs, they may pass through three different companies in countries on three different continents to fabricate, test, and package them before they are ready.[306] Therefore it is unlikely China will succeed in the next few years, or even the next ten years for CPUs and GPUs, in Xi's desire to achieve technological self-sufficiency in this field.

I asked Michael Dunne about potential Chinese vulnerabilities in the semiconductor industry. He admitted, "China is vulnerable there for sure." He continued by saying, "Both Nvidia and Qualcomm are deeply embedded in China already. If Chinese AV companies were to be cut off from chips and from that know-how, it would be a setback." Even with China's substantial increase in patents, this weakness has troubled the CCP and technology companies are trying to address it.

China has been desperately trying to address this issue. According to Taiwan's *Business Weekly*, China has poached over three thousand Taiwanese semiconductor engineers by offering them exorbitant salaries. Taiwan is one of the world leaders in semiconductor technology. This hiring of Taiwanese experts represents approximately ten percent of all Taiwanese people engaged in semiconductor research and development.[307]

Chinese semiconductor companies have also been sued for intellectual property theft. In one instance, US semiconductor company Micron sued Chinese SOE semiconductor company Fujian Jinhua for intellectual property theft. The

---

306 Kenneth Flamm, "Coping With Globalization in Semiconductors," *World Politics Review*, June 15, 2010.

307 Kensaku Ihara, "Taiwan loses 3,000 chip engineers to 'Made in China 2025,'" *Nikkei Asian Review*, December 3, 2019.

US government barred Jinhua from buying vital tools and materials for fabricating microchips.[308]

In a last-ditch effort, Jinhua offered to sell Micron the chip fabrication plant, or "fab." One of the principle shareholders of Jinhua argued, "It should be a pretty attractive proposition for Micron, because they gain access to a brand-new fab without having to invest billions. It should be attractive for a lot of manufacturers for that matter." This would not exactly make China less dependent on foreign manufacturers, but it would help it overcome potentially its greatest vulnerability in chip supply in the short term.[309]

Both the US and China have weaknesses. These weaknesses could slow down, or potentially halt, their respective autonomous vehicle industries. The US may be in a better position to overcome its weakness in lacking 5G infrastructure by importing it from other countries. The US also has companies, such as Cisco, which make similar infrastructure projects and could be incentivized to start making infrastructure for 5G networks.

Xi Jinping has the right idea of investing billions of dollars to address China's weak semiconductor industry but improving it will be very difficult. It is difficult to envision China being able to produce less complicated memory chips from its fabs in the next few years, let alone fabricating GPUs or CPUs for autonomous vehicles before the next ten years. China must rely on countries like the US for these chips.

This brings up the final potential weakness for China: the Chinese government.

---

308 Adam Rogers, "US Accuses Chinese Company of Stealing Micron Trade Secrets," *Wired*, November 1, 2018.

309 Ibid.

SLOW TO THE STARTING LINE BUT GAINING SPEED: CHINA'S AUTONOMOUS VEHICLE COMPANIES RACE TO BEAT THE US

Some final issues Michael Dunne discussed relate to the imbalance in foreign direct investment and access to technology between the US and China. He said, "Every year tens of billions of dollars of foreign direct investment flows into China, just making things so lucrative for so many Chinese businesses and people...and that's at risk of slowing dramatically."

He then described, based on his experience at GM, that until very recently this has not been the case for Americans doing business in China. American companies had to establish joint ventures with Chinese companies. This split the profit. With the import duties by China, a company needed to produce the vehicles in China and exchange technology with their JV partners. It is a totally uneven playing field and could change dramatically in the coming months and years. Mr. Dunne explained he talks to Chinese businesspeople about this trend. He tells them, "It might seem normal to them because they have grown accustomed to it, but it's uneven and it could end. And when I say that, they never even conceived of such a reality."

Mr. Dunne also brought up the technology sector, saying, "They've gotten used to almost unfettered access to the US market and technology. It's been carte blanche, wide open." With increased attention paid to this issue by the US government, Chinese people's access to US technology will be dramatically reduced in the coming months and years. This will continue to gain more attention and importance in the US as China continues to develop and export new technology around the world.

These two trends could dramatically change the Chinese technology and autonomous vehicle industries. They will need to be managed by Chinese companies effectively if they wish to survive and compete in the global race against their counterparts in the US. With the political strife between President Trump and Xi Jinping worsening, these companies would need to react to these changes sooner rather than later.

Xi's eagerness and ambition to succeed and make China a great power in East Asia and the world could impact the new Chinese tech sector and the autonomous vehicle industry. Along with pushing for autonomous vehicle development, the CCP has also been much more aggressive at home and abroad.

Arguing they pose a national security threat, Xi Jinping has ordered the detention of over one million ethnic minority Muslim Uighurs in camps in Xinjiang Province. This has damaged China's relationship with many European countries who value protection of human rights.[310] Before this, China could have formed closer relationships with European countries who were angry with President Trump for leaving the Paris Climate Accords and the Iran Nuclear Deal. However, actions against the Uighurs, along with other actions by the CCP against Hong Kong, weakened this potential benefit for China.

The CCP has sparked months of protests in Hong Kong because Hong Kong residents claim the CCP is not respecting Hong Kong's autonomy. This autonomy is part of the "One Country Two Systems" agreement. On June 30, 2020, China invoked a national security law. This law allows China to

---

310 Chris Buckley, "China Is Detaining Muslims in Vast Numbers. The Goal: 'Transformation'," *The New York Times*, September 8, 2018.

bypass Hong Kong's legislature and take more forceful action to break up protests. This includes arresting protestors. The CCP claims this action is justified because these protestors are "terrorists" who seek to cause unrest for no reason.[311]

US Secretary of State Mike Pompeo responded, saying Hong Kong was no longer autonomous and is part of China. Therefore, Hong Kong, and Chinese companies operating out of Hong Kong, might no longer be exempt from the various import tariffs imposed on China by the US.[312]

Hong Kong also has one of the most stable stock markets in Asia. However, the stock market suffered one of its largest single-day drops in the last five years after China imposed the national security law. Hong Kong's Heng Seng index dropped 5.6 percent. Continued efforts by China to exert control over Hong Kong could lead to further stock market declines and cause people to lose trust in the market.[313]

CHINESE TECH COMPANIES OFFER THE BEST CHANCE FOR THE CHINA DREAM TO BECOME A REALITY

China has incredibly talented tech companies, such as Alibaba and Tencent, who finance autonomous vehicle companies. Baidu is one of the largest tech companies in China and is also one of the major autonomous vehicle companies as well. Mr. Dunne backs my argument that companies in the US have better technology, but China has the advantage related to the relative ease of passing laws in China.

---

311 Chris Buckley and Keith Bradsher, "Brushing Aside Opponents, Beijing Imposes Security Law on Hong Kong," *The New York Times*, June 30, 2020.

312 Jennifer Hansler, Nicole Gaouette, and Kylie Atwood, "Pompeo says Hong Kong is no longer autonomous from China, jeopardizing billions of dollars in trade," *CNN*, May 27, 2020.

313 Noah Sin and Tom Westbrook, "Hong Kong stocks fall most since 2015 as Beijing pushes security law," *Reuters*, May 22, 2020.

Mr. Dunne said, "Never mind who's leading in technology innovation. To me it's where the rubber meets the road, where people are commercializing and making money for the business. In that regard, China is really trying to make it as easy as possible for deployment." The one caveat to his argument, was if China reverts back to relying on SOEs and not tech companies for the autonomous vehicle industry, and then he agrees with Dr. Economy that it will not go very far, very fast.

Chinese companies have created a revolutionary new mobile payment system. However, this system creates the worrying possibility of government economic surveillance of its population,

The investment in 5G network connections by companies such as Huawei and ZTE could allow the CCP to create global standards for this new technology and all of its seemingly limitless possible applications, but this technology has exacerbated tensions with the US in the escalating trade dispute.

The one flaw which could upset all of this is China's weak semiconductor industry. The ability to fabricate microchips is essential for technology companies generally, and autonomous vehicle companies specifically. Continued aggressive actions by the CCP at home and abroad could put this vital supply chain at risk. However, Xi Jinping is no longer "biding his time." He wants China to retake what he sees as its rightful place as the leader of Asia and as a global superpower.

It appears Xi Jinping and the CCP have learned their lesson from electronic vehicles and will not play too direct a role in the development of the autonomous vehicle industry. They will leave that up to the incredibly talented tech companies in China. Xi's increasingly aggressive actions in Hong Kong and naval vessel deployments to the disputed island chains in the

East and South China Seas have shocked Western observers. These moves could lead to legislation such as export controls for critical tech components. The China Dream, therefore, has the potential to turn into a nightmare.

CHAPTER 11

ROBIN LI AND BAIDU'S OPEN SOURCE APOLLO PROJECT: PROPHECY OR RECIPE FOR DISASTER?

THE PROPHET ROBIN LI LEADS THE APOLLO PROJECT FOR AUTONOMOUS VEHICLE SUPREMACY FOR CHINA

The first step in the marathon process of developing and producing autonomous vehicles can often be the hardest. What should the company's name be? What signals both the excitement and revolutionary nature of driverless vehicles? When deciding the name for his autonomous vehicle company, co-founder and CEO of Baidu, Robin Li, decided to channel a prophetic god's spirit and named it the Apollo Project.

The name refers to the Apollo 11 mission by NASA to reach the moon, but the name itself goes back thousands of years to ancient Greece. According to Greek mythology,

Apollo, the son of Zeus, was the god of prophesy.[314] The Apollo Project is certainly ambitious. Most companies in the autonomous vehicle industry are extremely secretive with their intellectual property. Baidu is the only major autonomous vehicle company to make Apollo open source (giving the data algorithms of the automated driving system) to all of its over one hundred thirty partners.[315]

These partners come from all over the world and from every aspect of the automotive ecosystem. They include automakers, tier one suppliers, component producers, startups, academic institutions, and even relevant government departments.[316] The goal is to accelerate the development of autonomous vehicles by opening the source code to allow for other partners to work on and test the Apollo Project's automated driving system.

By attempting to create this utopian system of many partners working together for one goal, Li is betting a lot of money on the shared altruism of different people. The supply chain for every autonomous vehicle company is global but opening the source code to his partners is unique to Baidu.

The Apollo Project presents great opportunities to reduce the R&D costs of autonomous vehicle development. It also creates significant risks. Cynics would point to the ancient Greek myth of Icarus as perhaps a more appropriate analogy.

Icarus flew from his prison cell on wings constructed by his famed inventor father and cellmate Daedalus. Daedalus constructed these wings from the discarded feathers of seagulls and other birds glued to leather wing frames

---

314 Mark Cartwright, "Apollo," *Ancient History Encyclopedia*, July 25, 2019.

315 Kyle Wiggers, "Baidu announces Apollo 3.5 and Apollo Enterprise, says it has over 130 partners," *Venture Beast*, January 8, 2019.

316 Ibid.

constructed from candle wax. Icarus's hubris caused him to ignore his father's instructions and fly too close to the sun. This melted the wax holding the feathers to the wings and he was sent plummeting to his death. Critics could argue Baidu is also displaying hubris in this partnership. Losing key partners could significantly affect the Apollo project's autonomous vehicle development.[317]

Convincing so many different companies to join one project requires a herculean effort by Robin Li. Automakers particularly would need to be persuaded to join in a project and not compete against Baidu. Meanwhile, academic institutions and government departments would need to set aside any disagreements or arguments against the Chinese Communist Party (CCP). Baidu is not an SOE, but it continues to have close ties to the government by censoring its search engine.

This chapter describes the perils of Western analysts misunderstanding the business and technological landscape of China. Because they do not understand the differences in the system, they tend to underestimate competing Chinese companies. Robin Li and Baidu represent just one example. His innovative approach to fostering an open-source partnership could put him in the driver's seat to lead China to victory over the US. If the partnership holds, that is.

MISUNDERSTOOD AND UNDERESTIMATED, THE PROPHET EMERGES

A closer examination of Robin Li's life history is necessary to gain a full picture of his vision for the Apollo Project.

---

317 Gabi Ancarola, "The Tragic Story of the Fall of Icarus," *Greek Reporter*, April 17, 2018.

Yanhong (Robin) Li was the fourth of five children, and the only boy. His parents both worked in a factory in Shanxi Province, China.[318]

As the only boy of the family's five children, Li was under pressure to succeed and provide for his sisters and parents. He strived to achieve success academically. His first success came when he was admitted to Peking University in 1987. At Peking University, he studied information sciences and received his BS in 1991.[319]

Li then travelled to the United States to pursue a PhD in computer science at the State University of New York (SUNY) in Buffalo in 1992. Unlike his fellow countryman, Jianxiong Xiao (Professor X), Li decided not to continue to earn a doctorate. Instead, he received his master's degree in computer science in 1994.[320]

Li began his professional career shortly after he graduated from SUNY Buffalo at IDD Information Services in 1994. IDD was the New Jersey division of Dow Jones and Company. In this job, he helped develop a software program for the online edition of *The Wall Street Journal*.[321]

It was at this job Li began to develop the expertise for search engines which would serve him well as CEO of Baidu. He created a program which was awarded a patent by the US government called Rankdex in 1996. Rankdex was a site-ranking search algorithm for search engine rankings. This program was the first to use hyperlinks to measure the

---

318 Garrett Parker, "10 Things You Didn't Know About Baidu Founder Robin Li," *Money, Inc.*, visited September 8, 2020.

319 Ibid.

320 Ibid.

321 "Robin Li's vision powers Baidu's Internet search dominance," *Taipei Times*, September 17, 2006.

quality of the websites it was indexing.[322] This program predated a similar program from Google by two years. Google founder Larry Page referenced Li's work several times in his patent applications.[323]

Fresh off his initial success in the burgeoning search engine development world, Li then decided to move to the mecca of the high-tech industry, Silicon Valley, in July 1997. In Silicon Valley, Li worked as a staff software engineer for pioneering search engine site Infoseek.[324]

At Infoseek, Li added to his stellar reputation as an innovator by developing the picture search function used by Go.com.[325] Li then left Infoseek to form his own company with his friend Eric Xu. They called the new company Baidu.[326]

When Li returned to China after founding Baidu, he began the battle for the internet search engine market. In this battle, he would be competing against many different Chinese startups and international challengers from Yahoo and Google.

The Chinese education system emphasizes rote memorization over creativity and developing problem-solving skills. This has led to criticism by Western observers that the education system does not foster a spirit of innovation to create new goods and services in China. However, Li was

---

322 Yanhong Li, "Towards a Qualitative Search Engine," *IEEE Internet Computing*, vol. 2, no. 4, pp. 24-29, July/August 1998.

323 James Altucher, "10 Unsurprising Things About Google (also: the worst VC decision I ever made)," *Forbes*, March 18, 2011.

324 Jonathan Watts, "The man behind China's answer to Google: accused by critics of piracy and censorship," *The Guardian*, December 9, 2005.

325 Ibid.

326 David Barboza, "The Rise of Baidu (That's Chinese for Google)," *The New York Times*, September 17, 2006.

both educated and began his career in the US. He received his postgrad education in the US. He also gained valuable experience and excelled in Silicon Valley. He decided to move Baidu to a region where he knew the customer base and could use the education and skills gained in the US to succeed.

I had a discussion with Dr. Matthew Johnson, founder and principal of business consulting firm AltiSilva LLC. In his work, Johnson directs and conducts research related to supporting China-focused advisory, due diligence, and risk management. He pointed to some of the US advantages in developing new technology. He said, "The US has invested in a system which produces the best technology in the world. It doesn't mean this technology is produced by SOEs."

This is another common critique of new technology development in China. The Chinese government supports corrupt and inefficient SOEs. Dr. Johnson continued, saying, "The United States has the deepest capital markets. It means the United States has the most business-friendly environment. It means the United States is the most welcoming to entrepreneurs of all nationalities." While this is all true, the potential consumer base for new products and services in China is enormous.

The lack of established companies in the tech sector also makes it easier for new companies to enter and succeed. Li returned, armed for battle against whatever competition he would face from both Chinese startups and foreign companies. The fight would be for the ultimate prize of winning the Chinese search engine market.

Foreign companies often fail to understand that Chinese consumers want different products and services than those which were successful in Western countries. No one thought the internet titan Google would fail when it entered China in 2006.[327] Robin Li recognized the significant differences between the people in China, their habits and consumer culture, and the need to establish relationships with the government. All of this would be essential to succeed in China.

Li succeeded, in part, by recognizing the distinct internet search patterns of Chinese people. This distinction was noted by Lee Kai-fu in his book *AI Superpowers: China, Silicon Valley, and the New World Order.* These search patterns differ greatly from the top-to-bottom approach people in the US and Europe prefer.[328]

Lee Kai-fu tracked search patterns for Chinese people when he was working at Google China. He did this by monitoring their eye movements to determine how long they looked at one part of the screen. He also looked at where they clicked a link. The results appeared as red dots on the screen. For Chinese people, the screen appears to have chicken pox, with people looking at and clicking on links all over the screen.[329] Baidu employed a condensed layout which made it much easier to use this approach.[330]

As any child or adult learner can tell you, Mandarin Chinese is an extremely complex language. The word order is different from English, and words can have many different meanings depending on the context in which they are used. There are also many abbreviations of words which could cause frustration for people if the search engine does not account for them.

---

327 Matt Sheehan, "How Google took on China – and lost," *MIT Technology Review*, December 19, 2018.

328 Kai-fu Lee, *AI Superpowers: China, Silicon Valley, and the New World Order*, New York: Houghton Mifflin Harcourt, 2018), 37.

329 Ibid. 37

330 Ibid. 38

Baidu's search engine algorithm was geared specifically for the complexities of Mandarin Chinese. Google, by contrast, could not create a similar search engine algorithm. Lee Kai-fu mentioned he pleaded with Google executives in Silicon Valley to alter its search engine layout and language algorithms, but he was ignored.[331]

Robin Li also recognized the political reality of doing business in China. He allowed the CCP access to Baidu's search engine algorithms to censor information. Baidu also allowed the Chinese government to block certain keywords from producing search results. Google, however, refused to allow the CCP to access its search engine algorithms. This was because of its belief in information openness. It also faced legal pressure and public relations backlash in the US if it did censor data.[332] Recognizing defeat, Google left China in 2010. Now, Baidu has between a seventy to eighty percent market share in China, compared to a paltry 3.7 percent by Google.[333]

There are some key points from this example. Li was underestimated by foreign competitors, particularly those from Silicon Valley. Li beat Google by eschewing their site layout and business strategy in favor of strategies matching the specific preferences of Chinese people. Finally, Li developed a strong relationship with the CCP, which is essential for doing business in China.

The next challenge for Robin Li and Baidu would be to transition away from focusing on perfecting its search engine. It would need to move to the extremely complicated task of developing and producing autonomous vehicles.

---

331 Ibid. 39

332 Matt Sheehan, "How Google took on China – and lost," *MIT Technology Review*, December 19, 2018.

333 "Search Engine Market Share China," *GlobalStats*, August 2020.

IN THE APOLLO PROJECT, LI SEEKS TO PROVE HIMSELF AGAIN

How did Robin Li switch from his success as an internet search engine entrepreneur to enter the autonomous vehicle industry? Before he launched Project Apollo, Baidu pivoted to become an artificial intelligence (AI) power in China.

In September 2005, Baidu released Little Fish. Little Fish was a home organizational device, similar to Amazon's Alexa or Google Home devices. The Little Fish device differs from Alexa or Google Home in that it also comes with a touch screen on top of its orb-shaped base. The touch screen can be used to purchase items and has other functions as well. While the device also has an advanced voice recognition algorithm similar to Alexa or Google Home, there is also the option of using the touch screen to control it.[334]

Before the Apollo Project, Baidu also had experience partnering with other companies. For example, they made an agreement with leading Chinese telecom provider China Unicom to apply AI and other leading technologies to their future mobile products and services.[335]

Creating the group of partners to provide assistance for its autonomous vehicle program in the Apollo Project followed a trend in the company. This does not represent an anomaly in Baidu's expanding AI business platform. Google has also been working on new technology "moonshot" projects. However, those are done at the secretive X labs and not as an open source platform. Li's next task would be his most difficult yet.

---

334 Paul Miller, "Baidu's 'Little Fish' home robot could be China's Echo," *The Verge*, January 5, 2017.

335 Jillian Olazo, "Baidu, China Unicom embark on AI partnership," *S&P Global*, November 3, 2016.

To accomplish this task, Li could not simply employ the same strategy which allowed him to beat Google in China, at least not if he intended to export this technology oversees. He would need to prepare his vehicles for global standards, not just standards which best suited doing business in China.

I discussed the challenges of creating safe autonomous vehicles that reach global standards with Dr. Johnson. He began by talking about the importance of standard setting in general. He said, "Standards help to legitimate the technology so that if you can prove that this technology performs up to these standards, it is therefore safe."

As discussed in my chapter on Xi Jinping's push to transform the Chinese economy by developing new technology, China is also actively seeking to set global standards for new technology. Dr. Johnson discussed why this could be important, saying, "When a company has a disadvantage of producing that 'safe' technology, or if the technology isn't that safe but becomes accepted, that allows them to compete on cost." He used the example of how drones make law enforcement cheaper because they can surveil large areas of land faster than it would take for police officers and at significantly reduced cost.

This situation also applies to autonomous vehicles. The CCP will almost certainly pass legislation and create standards for autonomous vehicles to be on the market on a large scale before the US. If China can succeed in setting the global standards for autonomous vehicles for safety, then Chinese companies would have the advantage.

Baidu's Apollo Project could make these vehicles cheaper as part of the Apollo Project defraying costs of developing autonomous vehicles to all of the partners. This is assuming the partnership stays intact. The CCP could also give them and other companies in the autonomous vehicle industry subsidies. These subsidies would allow Baidu, and other companies, the ability to sell their vehicles to emerging markets cheaper than companies from the US.

Robin Li recognized the magnitude of both developing the technology for autonomous vehicles and making them commercially viable. After all, he chose to name the project the Apollo project based on the revolutionary NASA Apollo missions to the moon.[336] The objective to make them commercially viable is a quest he shares with every other company in the autonomous vehicle industry.

Baidu is one of the leading technology companies in China, with tens of thousands of employees working in all parts of the company, but how can Baidu serve as the glue holding the partners together in order to perform this monumental challenge of developing autonomous vehicles?

Li defined the role of Baidu as maintaining the core functions of the autonomous vehicle. He stated, "We will develop and maintain the type of algorithms, models, and development tools and also all the high definition mapping for the streets."[337]

Essentially, after battling with Google for China's search engine supremacy, Robin Li is attempting to follow the path of Waymo. Baidu will create the core automated driving "brain" of the vehicle. They will then have the various hardware partners add the GPS, LiDAR sensors, cameras, radar, and more. This would leave it up to the OEM partners to decide whether, and at what time, to mass produce the

---

336 Yuxian Qiu, "Baidu Apollo Leads Self-Driving Advances," *Equal Ocean*, July 3, 2019.

337 Yufy Zhang, "Apollo: China's Autonomous Driving Program Explained," *EE Times Asia*, June 21, 2018.

vehicles. The Apollo Project differs from Waymo because there is an open platform for partners, all of the partners can contribute to testing their autonomous vehicles.

Robin Li and Baidu's allowing the CCP to access Baidu's search algorithms to censor any information created trust from the CCP. This government support helped the Apollo Project's efforts to develop autonomous vehicles. From the very beginning, the CCP recognized Baidu's importance. They called on Baidu to lead the way in AI innovation for self-driving cars in China.[338]

Baidu is also one of the few companies licensed to create high definition maps of city streets in China.[339] Creating these maps, as I discussed in my chapter on the "brain" of the autonomous vehicle, is vital for them to drive safely.

The government's faith in Baidu and the Apollo Project has already delivered some impressive milestones after only three years. In 2019, thirteen companies were granted licenses to test autonomous vehicles on public roads in Beijing. These vehicles combined to drive 1.04 million kilometers autonomously. Baidu drove by far the most with fifty-two vehicles driving 754,000 kilometers. The second-place company, Pony.ai, a startup founded by former Baidu autonomous vehicle executive James Peng, had six vehicles that drove 120,000 kilometers.[340]

This data did not show how many times the car had to disengage (have a human take control.) However, this is still

---

338 Ryan Gandolfo, "Baidu Leading the Way for Autonomous Driving in China," *that's Beijing*, November 5, 2018.

339 Xiaowei Wang, "How Baidu maps turn location data into 3-D cityscapes – and big profits," *The Architect's Newspaper*, May 17, 2019.

340 Kyle Wiggers, "77 autonomous vehicles drove over 500,000 miles across Beijing in 2019," *Ventura Beat*, March 2, 2020.

very impressive. This is especially impressive considering how chaotic city streets in Beijing can be. As anyone who has been to Beijing or any other city in China can attest, people constantly jaywalk, bicycles cut in and out between pedestrians and cars, cars weave between people as they cross, cars treat red lights as suggestions, and a cacophony of horns blare at all times.

"Edge cases," or cases in which people or drivers act irrationally, are far more common in China than in most places in the US. There may be several "edge case" per week driving a vehicle autonomously in California. However, there may be several per hour or per day in China. These "edge cases" result in millions of lines of code being added to the autonomous vehicle's data algorithms. With enough miles tested on Chinese roads, Baidu's Apollo Project vehicles could drive anywhere else in the world.

Baidu has also won bids in 2020 to test its autonomous vehicles in two cities. They have a test site in Chongqing, which has recently invested heavily in smart infrastructure.[341] They also have a site closer to Robin Li's hometown in the Yangquan Economic Development Zone in Shanxi Province.[342]

These two sites will test the Apollo Project vehicles' V2X (Vehicle to Infrastructure) capabilities. This includes connecting to roadside cameras or other sensors through a 5G data network. Testing the vehicle' V2X capability will assist them with object detection and recognition. If successful, these test sites would both improve Apollo vehicles' data

341 Jill Shen, "Baidu is building everything Chongqing needs for self-driving cars," *technode*, March 20, 2020.

342 Baidu, "How coronavirus is accelerating a future with autonomous vehicles," *MIT Technology Review*, May 18, 2020.

algorithm and could lead to more widespread adoption of smart infrastructure projects.

Robin Li represents a technology chameleon. He is willing to change the shape of his enterprises to best fit the products he is developing. He achieved his success in China by taking the search engine standard and localizing it. This localization allowed it to match the particular search preferences, language, and political situation in China. He is attempting to move from his local base and globalize the production of autonomous vehicles. His success or failure may depend on whether international trends of nationalism and anti-globalization weaken. The most pressing concern the current US-China trade war.

Li has been able to attract US partners, most notably Ford Automotive in 2018. Ford is one of the largest OEMs in the US. Sherif Marakby, president and CEO of Ford Autonomous Vehicles LLC, talked about his goal of joining the Apollo Project. He said, "Working with a leading tech partner like Baidu allows us to leverage new opportunities in China to offer innovative solutions that improve safety, convenience, and the overall mobility experience."[343]

Ford chose to partner with Baidu for the opportunity to enter what is now the largest auto sales market in the world. As one of the key partners, Ford's membership will be a crucial means by which Robin Li and Baidu can keep their existing partners and add new ones.

Baidu offers a strong incentive for companies in western countries to join the Apollo Project as a partner. That is the opportunity to enter the Chinese market. However, leaders

343 Ryan Gandolfo, "Baidu Leading the Way for Autonomous Driving in China," *that's Beijing*, November 5, 2018.

in the US and the U.K. could impose restrictions on their companies from joining a Chinese company.

Baidu and telecom giant Huawei, with its investment in 5G, represent the biggest threat for China to take the lead and win the race for autonomous vehicles. This unique, open-source partnership shows why Robin Li chose to name his company the Apollo Project. International tension, or the desire for companies to work alone, could cause the OEMs and other key hardware suppliers to break away.

Because of China's weak semiconductor industry, losing a microchip partner could also grind Baidu's development to a halt. Losing partners, particularly if many leave at once, would send Baidu's autonomous vehicle program crashing to the ground like Icarus. Because of his track record of success against all odds, it would be unwise to bet against Robin Li and Baidu.

CHAPTER 12

PROFESSOR X AND AUTOX: "DEMOCRATIZING" AUTONOMOUS DRIVING

THE PLAN: MAKE AUTONOMOUS VEHICLES AFFORDABLE TO EVERYONE

Jianxiong Xiao (later known as Professor X) faced a dilemma. How could he realize his dream to make rides on autonomous vehicles affordable to everyone, while still optimizing the vehicles to be as safe as possible?

Eventually he would arrive at the solution to own an 80,000-square-foot facility for your own company, AutoX, in Shanghai. The facility is equipped for his one hundred autonomous "robotaxis." The computers also run driving simulations 24/7 to improve the vehicles' deep-learning technology. Rides would be affordable for everyone and the profit margins would eventually be huge.[344]

This plan was still over three decades away for the poor boy living in a fishing village in Guandong Province, China.

Unlike the bustling business and technology centers of Guangzhou and Shenzhen in the nearby Pearl River Delta region, the village of Chaoshan lagged far behind in terms of industrial and commercial development. Still, Xiao became fascinated with computers. While he could not afford a computer himself, he read about them in books and learned to touch-type on a keyboard drawn on paper.[345]

Xiao later recalled his family was loving but so poor that, "My family never owned a car and we could not afford to travel to the beach for a vacation."[346] Over the years, Xiao developed a passion for providing mobility to everyone, regardless of how much money they had.

To establish himself, he would first need to acquire the skills and training to pursue these ambitions. He devoted himself to the incredibly competitive task of gaining admittance to a university in China. His first success came when he studied at Hong Kong University of Science and Technology. He excelled in his studies of computer science and received his Bachelor of Engineering (BEng) and Master of Philosophy (MPhil) degrees in 2009.[347]

The undergraduate admission process in China is famously competitive. Every person is required to take one

---

344 Catherine Shu, "AutoX launches its RoboTaxi service in Shanghai, competing against Didi pilot program," *TechCrunch*, August 17, 2020.

345 Yifan Yu, "Professor X readies self-drive cars for China's busy streets," *Nikkei Asian Review*, August 23, 2019.

346 Ibid.

347 Jianxiong Xiao, "Jianxiong Xiao (Proessor X)," jianxiongxiao.com, visited June 7, 2020.

高考, or "Big Test," which is held only once per year. This test determines what, if any, universities will accept them.[348]

The Chinese college admissions process is nothing compared to the startup competition in China. In the Chinese tech sector, there is what is called the "996" culture. Workers are expected to work from 9 a.m. to 9 p.m. six days per week. Jack Ma, co-founder and CEO of tech titan Alibaba, said working long hours was, "a huge blessing." This level of work ethic expectation would put self-proclaimed workaholics in Silicon Valley to shame. Tech workers are beginning to challenge this trend. Such an ingrained set of work standards will be very difficult to change, at least in the short term.[349]

Xiao decided to pursue the highest quality education he could to arm himself with the tools to beat all of his competitors. To do so, he would need to go to the US. He applied for and was accepted as a PhD student at MIT, one of the best technology schools in the world. He studied Computer Science at MIT from 2009 to 2013.[350]

As a PhD student, Xiao researched deep learning, the object recognition system described in my chapter about the "central nervous system" of the autonomous vehicle. Deep learning allows machines to perform difficult tasks such as recognizing people, cars, and things like trees, traffic cones, or mailboxes.[351]

Xiao also studied ways in which he could use just cameras at different angles to create a three-dimensional view of objects. He discovered ways he could accomplish this

---

348 Christina Larson, "The Big Test," *Foreign Policy*, June 10, 2011.

349 Qiqing Lin, "'996' is China's Version of Hustle Culture. Tech Workers Are Sick of It.," *The New York Times*, April 29, 2019.

350 "Jianxiong Xiao," *Credit Suisse*, March 28, 2020.

351 Ibid.

task regardless of the brightness of the light. The computer learning algorithms, combined with the cameras pointing at different angles, would later form the basis for autonomous driving vehicle technology.[352]

Of all of the CEOs of tech companies covered in this book, Xiao is the only person who received his PhD. Other major companies in the field, such as Waymo, Tesla, and Baidu have workers with PhDs in engineering or computer science. However, Xiao's in-depth knowledge of the technical challenges of this new technology separates him from his peers in this new field.

This knowledge allows him to more easily customize his autonomous vehicles for the different technological needs of the vehicle so he can design an ideal system for the vehicles to drive safely when they drive autonomously. The struggle would be for Xiao to find a way to commercialize autonomous vehicles while still fulfilling his goal of allowing everyone to ride them.

I interviewed a person who previously worked as part of the digital marketing team at NIO. NIO is a popular electric vehicle (EV) company in Shanghai. He began by telling me about the auto sales market in general in China. He said, "The auto industry has cycles, with upturns and downturns. And usually the cycle takes roughly ten years." He noted the Chinese case is different, saying, "In 2018, that was the first time in the past twenty years auto sales for passengers went down." Understanding the auto sales market in China, and different factors affecting it, is critical for the success of any vehicle manufacturing startup there. This would be true

352 Yifan Yu, "Professor X readies self-drive cars for China's busy streets," *Nikkei Asian Review*, August 23, 2019.

for companies manufacturing conventional vehicles, EVs, or autonomous vehicles.

China has a rising middle class and this was probably the first or second car people had purchased in their lives. Therefore, the number of total cars purchased would continue to rise for a longer time period than what would normally be expected before it experienced a downturn. Creating a plan to go to market in China was still just a future concern for Xiao, who was still in the US finishing his education and starting his career.

After graduating from MIT, Xiao accepted the job as an assistant professor at Princeton University. At Princeton, Xiao served as the principle director of the Princeton Computer Vision and Robotics Labs from 2013 to 2016.[353]

In this lab, Xiao was able to begin to test his theory that computer vision systems would allow a vehicle to see objects in 3D without using LiDAR sensors. It was at this point his students and work colleagues gave him his nickname "Professor X." His students and colleagues used this nickname because they had trouble pronouncing his Chinese name.[354]

PROFESSOR X VENTURES OUT ON HIS OWN TO PURSUE HIS GOALS

In 2016, Xiao faced perhaps the most difficult decisions of his life. He could continue his work as an academic at Princeton, where he was living in New Jersey with his mother and father and seek tenure.

After making a name for himself as someone adept at deep learning technology, he was also offered a job to lead

353 Ibid.

354 Ibid.

the autonomous driving research unit at Ford Automotive.[355] Working for one of the largest vehicle manufacturing companies in the world would provide him with the money and experience to expand his knowledge about how autonomous vehicles work.

He chose to quit his job at Princeton and declined the offer from Ford. Instead, he moved across the country to San Jose, California and created his own company with some seed funding and called his company AutoX.[356]

His decision to venture out on his own can be explained, at least in part, by remarks he made in a speech in 2017. He was named one of the "35 Under 35" by the *MIT Technology Review*. In his speech he said, "Autonomous driving should not be a luxury."[357] As an academic, he would not be able to pursue his goal of making autonomous vehicles because of all of the responsibilities associated with being a professor. He would need to teach classes, work with students and colleagues in the lab, publish articles in scientific journals, and also conduct his own research.

At Ford, he would not have control over the whole creative process of the vehicle. Everything from design, to which technology to use, to the final engineered product would already be decided for him. He would not be able to ensure the final product would be affordable for everyone. In the end, it would only be possible for him to achieve all of his goals if he started alone and used his knowledge of the field to build his own vehicle.

---

355 Ibid.

356 Tony Peng, "AutoX Wants to Put a Self-Driving Car in Your Driveway in Two Years," *Synced*, September 12, 2017.

357 Rachel Metz, "AutoX Has Built a Self-Driving Car That Navigates With a Bunch of $50 Webcams," *MIT Technology Review*, March 28, 2017.

Xiao clarified his statement about making autonomous driving not just a luxury when he described the strategy as "Democratizing Autonomous Driving." He compared autonomous vehicles to computers. Early on, computers were too large and expensive for people to buy. Over time, they became smaller and cheaper.[358]

Xiao then outlined all of the radar, LiDAR sensors, ultrasonic, and cameras currently used by other companies in their autonomous vehicles. He said these companies had "blind faith" in the necessity of LiDAR sensors for autonomous vehicles.[359]

Xiao showed a video demonstration of an AutoX vehicle driving during the day, at night, and even while it was raining heavily using only cameras in San Jose and Cupertino, California. He stated AutoX is not necessarily against other sensors, but they adopted a camera-based technique that still allows the vehicle to drive safely. This approach makes it more affordable.[360]

Now Xiao had a formula in place to make his autonomous vehicles more affordable and he would need a business and development strategy to make this dream a reality. He would need to grow his company from the ground up, hire skilled mechanics and computer engineers, and secure funding to move forward. The journey began in a small house in San Jose, California.

---

358 Jianxiong Xiao, "Democratizing Autonomous Driving," March 27, 2017, *MIT Technology Review,* Massachusetts Institute of Technology, speech, 32:10.

359 Ibid.

360 Ibid.

BUILDING AUTOX FROM A "ONE-MAN ARMY" TO A FLOURISHING BUSINESS

In many ways, the early days of AutoX resemble the beginning of Apple Computers. Steve Jobs and Steve Wozniak designed and coded the original Apple computer in Steve Jobs' garage.[361] Professor X worked feverishly by himself in a one-family house in San Jose. He lived and worked there with his parents.

Referring to this early stage of the company, he said, "I was a one-person army back then." He quickly added more employees to AutoX. He was a pioneer as a Chinese person developing exciting autonomous driving technology. Chinese and Chinese American scientists came from companies and universities which invested heavily in artificial intelligence. These places included MIT, IBM, and Facebook.[362]

Now, AutoX has grown into a company with over one hundred thirty people and has funding from companies such as the Chinese tech giant Alibaba.[363] The founder and CEO of Alibaba, Jack Ma, also came from a poor family and worked his way to become one of the richest men in the world. It is likely he saw a man in Xiao with the same fighting spirit and intelligence to succeed.

Xiao repeatedly states in interviews safety is the number one priority for autonomous driving technology. He says machines have the advantage of not getting tired, distracted, or drunk.[364] All of these things impair a human driver's ability to drive safely.

---

361 Megan Chovanec, "My grandma's Los Altos garage is where Apple was created," *Business* Insider, January 31, 2015.

362 Yifan Yu, "Professor X readies self-drive cars for China's busy streets," *Nikkei Asian Review*, August 23, 2019.

363 Ibid.

364 Chua Kong Ho and Sarah Dai, "China's Professor X says we are at the tipping point for mass roll-out of self-driving cars after tech advances,"

Xiao also said there are currently no more outstanding technological issues of autonomous driving technology that have yet to be resolved. However, there still needed to be work on coding for irregular activity "edge cases." At AutoX, he said, "We even run simulations to test the cars themselves with no satellite reception and without 5G access, using only the technology in the car as the worst-case scenario." This is in response to critics who say autonomous vehicles require things like LiDAR sensors to drive safely.[365]

Xiao stayed in the US near the technology center of Silicon Valley to build AutoX. He has said the Chinese technology sector has improved dramatically in recent years and is catching up to the US. However, he describes how it is not there yet and the best engineers and computer engineers are in the US. As a case in point, the first group of recruits who joined AutoX were Chinese, but they had come to the US to experience the better educational and monetary benefits of working at tech firms. This was not an option for them in China at the time.[366]

More companies have clearance for autonomous "robotaxis" now. However, back in June 2019, AutoX was one of only four companies to receive the clearance from the California DMV. Xiao did not want to transport people and instead only offered grocery deliver services to a limited area. When asked why he did not want to have his cars serve as "robotaxis," he replied, "We applied for the robotaxi license just to prove that we can do it and add credibility to our technology."[367]

South China Morning Post, September 11, 2019.

365 Ibid.

366 Yifan Yu, "Professor X readies self-drive cars for China's busy streets," *Nikkei Asian Review*, August 23, 2019.

367 Ibid.

Xiao is a maverick, not just for his decision to turn down a job at Ford in favor of starting his own company, but also for staying in the US instead of returning to China. In China, he could pay his employees significantly less money. He also knew the Chinese market better. His reluctance to start his "robotaxi" service in California can, in hindsight, be seen as a desire to return to China and pursue his ambitions there instead.

Before Shanghai came through with its offer to host AutoX in the massive facility, Xiao returned to China in 2019 to test and search for a new home for his company. Driving conditions in China are notoriously chaotic. A video in August 2019 demonstrated the capabilities of an AutoX vehicle, when the vehicle drove through a section of downtown Shenzhen. Shenzhen is a tech capital of China where tech giants like Huawei, Tencent, and Baidu all have offices.[368]

The AutoX vehicle successfully drove through cars suddenly stopping, pedestrians jaywalking in an area with no traffic lights, and scooters running red lights. At that time, AutoX was the only company in China to test its autonomous vehicle in a busy metropolitan area.[369]

Xiao also developed a good relationship with the Shenzhen city government to allow AutoX to test their vehicles in the city. Developing good relationships with local party leaders is essential to doing business in China. Xiao could readily understand this difference from the US, which might confuse and frustrate foreign companies. This was seen with Google at the national level, leading to it losing to Baidu for the search engine market, as discussed last chapter.

---

368 Ibid.

369 Ibid.

In China, your 关系, or "relationships," with people operate like currency. Local Chinese officials work cautiously, particularly with autonomous vehicles. Forming good relationships with officials helps grease the wheels in an otherwise hesitant bureaucracy. This allows for things to move faster for a company. Xiao demonstrated this with AutoX.[370]

Xiao displayed this same tactic with his next idea, getting the approval for his massive "robotaxi" facility in Shanghai and approval to drive one hundred "robotaxis" in Jiading District. In speeches and interviews, he always appears confident even though he lacks the innate charisma of the CEO of NIO, William Li, who news outlets call "the Elon Musk of China." In fact, after he was named to the "Innovators Under 35" list under the category of Entrepreneur, Xiao said, "For the first time, I was recognized as an entrepreneur! I think that's a better fit for me."[371]

Xiao came from learning to touch type on a fake keyboard drawn on a piece of paper to becoming a renowned computer science professor at Princeton University. Now an innovative entrepreneur with his own company, he chooses to follow his own path.

Xiao eschews the autonomous vehicle industry's "blind faith" in expensive LiDAR sensors in favor of his own camera-based system. Other than AutoX's major backer Alibaba Group Holdings, AutoX has also secure funding and support

---

370 PoN Staff, "The Importance of Relationship Building in China," *Harvard Law School: Program on Negotiations Daily Blog*, October 14, 2019.

371 Tony Peng, "AutoX Wants to Put a Self-Driving Car in Your Driveway in Two Years," *Synced*, September 12, 2017.

from MediaTek, and Chinese automakers Shanghai Auto and Dongfeng Motor.[372]

Because of this success, in the not-too-distant future Xiao aims to make it possible for even poor families to travel to the beach for a vacation.

The final section of this book discusses the political dilemma still facing the US at both the local, state, and national level to govern autonomous vehicles. Once there is adequate regulation in place in the US, it must turn its attention to the global arena for the battle over standards with China for this new technology. With no uniform set of standards, a "One Globe, Two Systems" scenario could emerge, leading to increased tension and perhaps violence between countries in these two "systems." The book concludes with a summary of the main themes discussed in this book as well as a brief glimpse ahead of what may be coming further down the road.

372 Catherine Shu, "AutoX launches its RoboTaxi service in Shanghai, competing with Didi's pilot program," *TechCrunch*, August 17, 2020.

PART 4:

NEXT STEPS AND LOOKING AHEAD

CHAPTER 13

POLICIES NEEDED TO PAVE THE WAY FOR AN AUTONOMOUS VEHICLES VICTORY FOR THE US

THE POLITICAL PROBLEM AND ADVOCATES AT THE LOCAL LEVEL

"Autonomous cars are the greatest step change in humanity since the Industrial Revolution."[373]

MARC HOAG, LICENSED ATTORNEY, STARTUP FOUNDER, AND HOST OF THE POPULAR PODCAST "AUTONOMOUS CARS WITH MARC HOAG"

---

373 Tracy Hazzard, "'How to Become the Center of Influence Through Podcasting and Validating Niche Expertise' with Marc Hoag of Autonomous Cars," *Authority Magazine*, May 15, 2019.

"Autonomous vehicles are nowhere near as smart as they need to be. Safety features – including manual override – must be top priority."[374]

US SENATOR RICHARD BLUMENTHAL

These two quotes indicate the vast differences of opinion in the US about autonomous vehicles. Some people see the potential safety and efficiency benefits of autonomous vehicles. Some skeptics believe it is impossible for a machine to drive a vehicle as safe, or safer, than a person.

In reality, there is a spectrum of opinions. Different organizations and groups of people argue over the merits of both viewpoints. These battles start at the local level but they can have a profound impact on the direction, or lack thereof, of policies related to autonomous vehicles at the state and national level in the US.

The US autonomous vehicle industry has the best technology in the world. Waymo leads a group of innovative companies. However, the automotive sector is one of the most regulated sectors in the US. Vehicles themselves are regulated at the national level. States regulate the drivers, with things like licensing, registration, insurance, and liability. Autonomous vehicle companies need to clear two political hurdles just to reach the road. Cooperation is the key to achieving a successful political outcome related to autonomous vehicles.

These policy making challenges give China the advantage to be the first to roll out large scale commercial use for autonomous vehicles. Just because Chinese companies will

---

374 Richard Blumenthal (@SenBlumenthal), Autonomous vehicles are nowhere near as smart as they need to be. Safety features – including manual override – must be top priority," Twitter, April 3, 2018, 3:51p.m.

be first doesn't mean the technological quality will be ready for the demanding task of driving autonomously on chaotic Chinese roads.

The slower but more measured US political reality would allow for greater quality. The greater quality of the vehicles would lead to the full range of potential benefits of autonomous vehicles. This would also make it easier for the US to export them and for the US to set the global standards for autonomous vehicles. There remains a steep political hill to climb to reach this point. However, passionate advocates are pushing for autonomous vehicles in the US at the grassroots, state, and national levels.

This chapter describes the political difficulties the US faces in regulating autonomous vehicles. Cooperation between different groups at the local level can lead to better advocacy efforts at the state and national level. By expanding the number of people interested in promoting autonomous vehicles, this increases the funds and bargaining power of their ideas.

The benefits of cooperation on many levels may seem utopian. However, because autonomous vehicles will benefit many different industries and people, cooperation is both pragmatic and essential for the success of the autonomous vehicle industry. Cooperation between members of state legislatures, members of the autonomous vehicle industry, and insurance company representatives in a "task force" would lead to better policy at the state level. This would allow for each group to ensure that their interests and concerns are being taken into account.

Congressmen and senators at the national level would also need to work together to create effective laws governing things like safety for autonomous vehicles. Government agencies would need to move from fighting with each other and work together to further the industry's development.

Finally, many different countries would need to advocate for a single set of standards for autonomous vehicles. This would allow them the greatest potential positive impact and avoid the "One Globe, Two Systems" scenario. This could be the result of further de-escalation of security and trade tensions between China and the US.

IT TAKES A VILLAGE TO BUILD AN AUTONOMOUS VEHICLE INDUSTRY: IMPACT AT THE LOCAL LEVEL

The Coalition for Future Mobility (CFM) is a highly diverse coalition of nearly fifty different groups advocating for the testing and deployment of autonomous vehicles in the US. These groups represent senior citizens, people with disabilities, safety advocates, environmental groups, and groups from the automotive and technology industries.[375] The bills introduced in the US House and Senate related to autonomous vehicles failed to become laws, but the CFM advocated for both bills in Congress.[376] They continue to grow as an organization with even the American Chemistry Council's Plastics Division joining on April 1, 2019.[377]

With more groups joining the CFM with a wide range of constituency groups, their lobbying and advocacy efforts to Congress on behalf of autonomous vehicles will continue to improve. This makes future bills more likely to pass. Even

---

375 "Coalition Members," *Coalition for Future Mobility*, visited September 10, 2020.

376 David Shepardson, "Self-driving car advocates launch ad campaign to prod Congress," *Reuters*, September 26, 2017.

377 Jennifer Killinger, "ACC Joins Coalition for Future Mobility," *American Chemistry Council*, April 1, 2019.

with the increased partisanship in the US Congress, autonomous vehicles are not a strong partisan issue and should not arouse significant opposition. Members of Congress must work together to create bills which address all, or most, of the needs of both the autonomous vehicle industry as well as all other groups represented by such organizations as the CFM.

The best way to get Congress to support and pass a law remains getting the public to trust and accept autonomous vehicles. This public push would also lead state legislatures to create pilot programs for testing them for things like university or airport shuttles or limited range autonomous vehicle "robotaxi" fleets.

I discussed in my chapter highlighting the potential benefits of autonomous vehicles that organizations for the blind are working with autonomous vehicle companies to make their vehicles accessible to blind people. They also advocate for legislation for autonomous vehicles at both the state and national level. Passionate grassroots organizations also advocate for autonomous vehicles. They arrange educational and networking events which form a community of like-minded people.

I spoke with Kevin Schlosser, the co-founder and president of one of these groups, the DC Autonomous Vehicle Association (DC-AVA). He discussed why he formed DC-AVA and the benefits these types of organizations have on educational and advocacy efforts for autonomous vehicles.

The story he recalled about why he is passionate about autonomous vehicles is tragic and, unfortunately, very common. He revealed, "In September 2017, I lost my girlfriend, Michelle Crowe, in a crash." Her car was hit by a truck driver who may have fallen asleep at the wheel. Schlosser then described how this was not the first time he had to deal with a situation like this. He recalled, "When I was twelve, my mother was also involved in a fatal car crash. Fortunately, my mother survived. However, her friend did not." He told how his mother suffered greatly from PTSD as a result of the accident. He could see her struggle and how it changed her personality.

He described, "After seeing my mother in the hospital bed when I was twelve and my girlfriend in a morgue for the exact same reason, there's no option for me. I have to do something." His advocacy efforts bring together many different people. Maybe not all of them have a passion derived from tremendous personal grief like him. However, they all believe autonomous vehicles can make their lives better.

Efforts by large, umbrella organizations like the CFM provide a template for more effective advocacy efforts at the city, state, and national level. They demonstrate that there is a large constituency of groups and individuals who would benefit from the deployment of autonomous vehicles on public roads and see them as having the potential to be safer than human-driven vehicles. Regional organizations also provide vital insight about how groups within regions or cities that otherwise might be overlooked have their agenda heard by policymakers. These regional groups can also work together to expand their outreach efforts.

DC-AVA and Self-Driving Cars 101 from San Francisco partnered for a virtual event, "How Policy Drives the Future of Autonomous Vehicles," on May 12, 2020.[378] These groups brought together the technical and engineering experts from

378 Chris Roberts and Kevin Schlosser, "How Policy Drives the Future of Autonomous Vehicles," *D.C. Autonomous Vehicles* Association, May 12, 2020.

San Francisco and political advocacy workers in the Washington, DC area. They talked about the policy dynamics people in San Francisco would like to see and the political reality of what the situation actually looks like from the panelists from Washington, DC.

The main lesson learned from local, regional, and national groups in their advocacy efforts related to autonomous vehicles is cooperation benefits everyone. In advocacy efforts at both the state and national level, there will be groups and organizations pushing to create comprehensive laws governing autonomous vehicles. Combined efforts by groups of people highlight the substantial number of individuals that are interested in having autonomous vehicles on the road. It also demonstrates the many different organizations that would benefit from them.

STATES AS THE "LABORATORIES OF DEMOCRACY" FOR AUTONOMOUS VEHICLES

As of the time of this writing, thirty-eight states and Washington, DC have passed laws and/or governors have issued executive orders regarding the operation of autonomous vehicles on public roads. Of these thirty-eight states, twelve states only allow for testing while sixteen and DC allow for full deployment of autonomous vehicles. The remaining twelve states do not have either laws or executive orders from their governors.[379]

The Department of Transportation (DoT) and the National Highway Traffic Safety Administration (NHTSA) issue periodic updates for guidelines for autonomous vehicles. However, there can be vastly different interpretations of these

---

379 "Autonomous Vehicles," *GHSA*, visited September 10, 2020.

guidelines between states. For example, even basic definitions of "vehicle operator" have differences in interpretations.[380]

For Tennessee this "operator" means the vehicle's Automated Driving System (ADS) with no need for an actual human backup driver. Texas describes the need for a "natural person" riding in the driver's seat. Meanwhile, Georgia only recognizes the operator as someone who activates the car's ADS. This means the car could be part of a fleet of vehicles and would not necessarily need a human backup driver in the driver's seat if someone from the other vehicle could remotely take over that vehicle.[381]

This confusing patchwork of state laws currently provides the only governing structure in the US for autonomous vehicles. For trips between two different states, there could be very different laws governing autonomous vehicles. To make matters worse, there could be a situation in which a neighboring state does not have a law passed. This would make driving in an autonomous vehicle between these two states illegal.

One particular case comes to mind related to interstate travel, with New York having laws governing autonomous vehicles, while New Jersey does not. While not everyone commutes to work by vehicle, hundreds of thousands of people cross state lines between New York and New Jersey every day. Therefore, it is vital for New Jersey to pass laws governing autonomous vehicles if the tri-state region wants autonomous vehicles in the near future.

I talked to Avi Kelin, chair of the Autonomous Vehicles Law Practice at the law firm Genova Burns in New Jersey. In the interview, we talked about the process of getting a law

---

380 Jack Karsten and Darrell West, "The state of self-driving car laws across the US," *Brookings Institute*, May 1, 2018.

381 Ibid.

governing autonomous vehicles passed in the state legislature. He expressed his frustration that New Jersey does not have any laws regulating autonomous vehicles. He said, "The strongest argument now for New Jersey to consider legislation whether you're in favor or opposed is right now, New Jersey has nothing."

This remark stood out to me because even people opposed to autonomous vehicles would still want to have standards governing them. This is particularly true because semiautonomous vehicles, such as vehicles with lane keep assist and adaptive cruise control, are currently driven in New Jersey.

One of the most interesting ideas he mentioned about the work he does to advocate for autonomous vehicle legislation in the New Jersey state government was his work on the New Jersey Advanced Autonomous Vehicle Task Force. He described this task force, saying, "Part of the beauty of the task force was there was a broad range of stakeholders involved. Everyone from New Jersey state officials, and the head of the motor vehicles commission in New Jersey."

He then described the task force was broadened to include an attorney (himself), engineering representatives, policy experts related to vehicles, and insurance representatives. Just like the CFM, inclusion of different people representing different areas all interested in autonomous vehicles would work to pass legislation. Creating this task force represents a step in the right direction to law formulation and passage.

Another issue related to the autonomous vehicle industry at the state level relates to issues of civil and criminal liability and auto insurance. With conventional vehicles, blame can be relatively easily determined. It will be the driver of one of the two vehicles in the accident. With autonomous vehicles, the situation becomes more complex. The blame could be with the automated driving system of the vehicle, a faulty sensor or camera, worn-out brake pads, or a backup driver not paying attention to the road, leading to a collision.

I talked to the vice president of an insurance carrier. She is in charge of the day-to-day execution of their strategy and tactics. She explained how, right now, they have to deal with all of the states separately if they want to change their insurance policy.

With autonomous vehicles that could change. She mentioned, "These manufacturers might not want to deal with fifty different insurance departments which might have a shift toward a federal law and regulations." However, there could just be a federal review board or committee. These issues could be discussed and gain the approval of the states to maintain the state's role in creating insurance and liability premiums.

On questions related to liability, I asked her if the Uber crash which killed Elaine Herzberg in 2018 would be used as precedent. She said, "This was one of the earlier cases and this will be used as a precedent so if cases occur in the future, lawyers are going to point back to this." I agree this will probably be the case, but this particular case has not yet been resolved completely. The vehicle operator has been charged with criminal negligence, but the court date for her trial is not until February 2021. While I hope that accidents do not happen, further cases may be necessary to establish a clearer precedent.

States have been called the "Laboratories of Democracy" by US Supreme Court Justice Louis Brandeis.[382] He was channeling a sentiment from the *Federalist Papers* written over one hundred fifty years ago in 1788 when he made this

---

382 Bradley A. Blakeman, "States are the laboratories of democracy," *The Hill*, May 7, 2020.

ruling.[383] These "laboratories" are valuable for testing laws. Because autonomous vehicles represent a new, and potentially dangerous and even fatal technology, states serve a critical role before things like safety standards are established at the national level.

Former internet pioneer and current autonomous vehicle advocate Brad Templeton compared the current test programs in Arizona and Silicon Valley to student drivers. He reported, "The driving-instructor is there to grab the wheel or hit the brakes if the teenager does badly. And the cars do make mistakes because they are just prototypes."

This could be cause for concern because student drivers can be erratic and unpredictable. Mr. Templeton also said the accident record is actually quite good. The hesitation to impose safety standards at the national level was echoed by Dr. Sven Beiker. He pointed out safety regulations should also concern traffic safety. This would include such things as how fast they drive and not necessarily just the vehicle safety. Therefore, it may be slightly premature to create regulation at the national level. It will be necessary in the long run for the industry to advance.

While states serve as the "Laboratories of Democracy," autonomous vehicle companies need clearer guidelines from the national government about how to test these vehicles. Different interpretations of guidelines cannot occur if goods or people are driven between different states. The task force Mr. Kelin works on provides an interesting way for cooperation to happen to achieve the best possible policy outcome. This is unlikely to work at the national level, however, where different factors need to be considered.

---

383 Ibid.

REGULATING THE AUTONOMOUS VEHICLES THEMSELVES BY THE CONGRESS AND THE EXECUTIVE BRANCH

The history of the federal government's legislative oversight over vehicles goes back over fifty years. Seat Belt Assemblies, requiring all vehicles have seat belts, was the first standard for the Federal Motor Vehicle Safety Standards (FMVSS).[384] This standard was created on March 1, 1967. Many more standards have been added since then. While this was the first time it was codified in a law, the federal government was widely considered to have oversight over the vehicles themselves and vehicle safety specifically.[385]

The Department of Transportation (DoT) has said repeatedly they do not favor any technology over another. They adopt a "tech neutral" approach to managing the US's transportation system.[386] However, new technologies like the autonomous vehicle, need government funding, or at least support, to pass new laws to spur the technology's development.

People in the autonomous vehicle industry are not asking for a dramatic overhaul of the laws governing vehicles in the US. I spoke with someone in the industry who is heavily involved in the legislative process but has asked his name and work affiliation be kept anonymous. He said they have asked for greater clarity from the federal government on its guidelines related to autonomous vehicles, more exemptions than the 2,500 vehicles currently allowed to each company, and an expedited process of creating updated standards in the FMVSS.

---

384 "Federal Motor Vehicle Safety Standards and Regulations," *Department of* Transportation, March 1, 1967.

385 Ibid.

386 Rob Stumpf, "Trump Wants Nothing to Do With 'Crazy' Driverless Cars," *The Drive*, March 18, 2019.

A friend of mine who works on these issues in Congress described the problems. She said there are huge hurdles to establishing autonomous vehicle regulation at the national level. For example, shared autonomous vehicles (SAVs) programs have problems because they don't meet some of the FMVSS rules. Many of these standards do not apply to autonomous vehicles. For example, the FMVSS requires all vehicles have side mirrors, rearview mirror, and a steering wheel. Assuming the technology is fully mature, none of these things would be necessary in an autonomous vehicle.

She agreed operating an SAV pilot program increases public trust in autonomous vehicles. She compared the issue to a "chicken and egg problem. People won't trust autonomous vehicles if they haven't had any experience riding in one, but people can't get that experience because of outdated laws."

At this time, autonomous vehicles still have things like a steering wheel, side mirrors, and rearview mirrors because the technology to drive autonomously still needs to mature. There still remains some issues that specifically relate to human drivers that autonomous vehicles cannot comply with.

The current 2,500 vehicle exemptions of the FMVSS is not a significant problem with autonomous vehicles still in the testing and R&D stage in their development. However, autonomous vehicle companies want an expanded list of exemptions because it would be impossible to commercialize these vehicles with only 2,500 vehicles per company.

Preemption often gets mentioned (no state can create tougher laws than the federal law), but the autonomous vehicle industry really just wants greater clarity on the standards. This would resolve the problem with states and different interpretations of "driver."

Finally, the companies in the autonomous vehicle industry do not want to create an entirely new set of regulations for autonomous vehicles. They want to have an expedited review process for incorporating autonomous vehicles into the existing FMVSS. For example, autonomous vehicles can include all of the current standard items because it doesn't make sense to push to remove them. Updating the FMVSS can take seven to eight years and they only want to focus on the standards that specifically refer to a human driver.[387]

There have been two proposed bills in 2017. One started in the House and one the Senate. The House bill passed in the House because it was very tightly conceived and only had the three policy preferences from the autonomous vehicle industry. It passed with bipartisan support.[388]

However, once it reached the Senate, it failed to get the required votes to become a law. The Senate typically moves slower than the House. For instance, every time an addition is added to the bill, it can take three months to argue each addition. Therefore, the bills can either run out of time before the Congressional term ends or fail to receive the votes to pass. In this case, a tight bill with bipartisan support became a bill with many partisan additions and the support gradually deteriorated until it ended in failure.[389]

Problems at the national level do not just exist in the Congress. One of the biggest hot button issues related to intra-governmental conflict in the US right now concerns the 5.9GHz frequency band for dedicated short-range

---

387 Marc Scribner, "Congress Must Help Modernize Outdated Auto Safety Regulations," *Competitive Enterprise Institute*, January 9, 2018.

388 Ryan Beene, "Bipartisan Autonomous Vehicle Legislation Stalls on Capital Hill," *Insurance Journal*, November 2, 2018.

389 Ibid.

communications (DSRC). The 5.9GHz frequency band for DSRC was created in 1999 for the DoT. Using DSRC, autonomous or connected vehicles can use wireless data transmission to communicate with other vehicles and smart infrastructure like smart stoplights or roadside cameras. The DoT retains exclusive rights to use this frequency band because of the benefits to safety and the reduction of traffic congestion.[390]

However, chairman of the Federal Communications Commission (FCC) Ajit Pai, proposed taking over half of the 5.9GHz frequency band for unlicensed equipment, such as Wi-Fi hotspots.[391] OEMs and other autonomous vehicle companies rely on the full 5.9GHz spectrum band for the vehicle's communications.

This is a problem because the more people using it, the longer a DSRC signal takes to be sent and return to the vehicles. This would make autonomous vehicles less safe and all of the possible reduction of traffic congestion benefits would be reduced. The battle over the 5.9GHz frequency band has not yet been resolved, but it is something to follow closely because it could significantly damage the autonomous vehicle industry.

Autonomous vehicles are a disruptive technology. They have the potential to disrupt many different industries in the US. Cooperation between different government agencies is essential. For instance, there has been positive cooperation between agencies within the DoT and department of Labor (DoL) on working to incorporate the needs of people

---

390 Bevin Fletcher, "FCC looks to dedicate 5.9GHz for Wi-Fi, C-V2X use," *Fierce Wireless*, November 20, 2019.

391 Ibid.

with vision problems into standards related to autonomous vehicles.[392]

There could also be cooperation between the Department of Education (DoE) and DoT or DoL to ensure that effective job retraining programs are created for people who risk losing their job due to the introduction of autonomous vehicles (such as taxi drivers and delivery van drivers). Current and new job training programs will help to ensure the success of this vital new technology in the US.

Autonomous vehicles represent a revolutionary new way to travel and transport goods, but the autonomous vehicle industry does not want to create new and revolutionary standards for laws that would regulate these vehicles. The more cooperation between different people, organizations, and companies, the stronger the roll-out of these vehicles will be. Enhancing cooperation between different government agencies will also help manage the changes that will come. All of this cooperation will be vital when it comes to competing with China on the global stage.

THE WORLD IS THE STAGE AND THIS COMPETITION HAS LASTING SIGNIFICANCE

Before and after President Donald Trump took office, a common rallying cry in his tweets and speeches was "America First!" This broad slogan generally refers to a foreign policy emphasizing nationalism, unilateralism, protectionism, and isolationism, all of this pursed in the interests of the US.[393] This turned out to be not just a slogan. The policies it

---

392 Doug Shinkle, "Crafting Inclusive Autonomous Vehicle Policies," *Our American States*, April 3, 2020.

393 Jenna Johnson, "What does 'America first' really mean?," *The Washington Post*, April 27, 2018.

promotes have been implemented by President Trump. The outcome for "winning" the race for autonomous vehicles, of setting the global standards for autonomous vehicles, has suffered accordingly.

Throughout the 2016 presidential campaign, President Trump railed against treaty arrangements that his predecessor, Barack Obama, signed with other countries. These treaties included the Paris Climate Accords.[394] This was an international agreement designed to reduce global greenhouse gas (GHG) emissions. This agreement was designed to lessen the potentially devastating human and economic damage of climate change.

Trump also objected to the Iran nuclear deal to limit Iran's nuclear power program. When he officially withdrew from the Iran deal on May 8, 2018, he said, "The heart of the Iran deal was a giant fiction: that a murderous regime desired only a peaceful nuclear energy program."[395]

On June 6, 2016, Trump had particularly harsh words directed at the Trans-Pacific Partnership (TPP) trade agreement. He said, "The Trans-Pacific Partnership is another disaster done and pushed by special interests who want to rape our country." He withdrew from the TPP right after he was officially sworn in as president in January 2017.[396]

President Trump comes from a business background. He leads an extensive real estate empire with hotels, casinos, and golf courses all over the world. Therefore, he treats

---

394 Alexandra Alper and Timothy Gardner, "Trump promotes pulling US from Paris climate accord in speech touting 'America First'," *Reuters*, October 23, 2019.

395 Mark Landler, "Trump Abandons Iran Nuclear Deal He Long Scorned," *The New York Times*, May 8, 2018.

396 Adam Taylor, "A timeline of Trump's complicated relationship with the TPP," *The Washington Post*, April 13, 2018.

relationships between countries like a contractual business partnership. He celebrates accomplishments, such as a revised Canada-US-Mexico Agreement (USMCA).[397] He also celebrates bilateral trade agreements with Japan and the slightly revised US-Korea Free Trade Agreement with South Korea.[398]

He celebrates these deals that bring short term benefits to the US. However, formal or informal alliances base on contractual terms can more easily be broken by competing arrangements from rival countries like China. Alliances built on shared historical, cultural, political, and ideological similarities last longer. The bonds between the countries are also more difficult to break.

Trump pressured NATO and other long-time US allies into contributing more money and placing import tariffs on goods and raw materials from the EU and other allies making the alliance weaker.[399] This weakening of alliances hurts US foreign, diplomatic, and economic policy in the long term.

The US is also taking a less active role in international organizations. The US withdrew its membership from the UN Human Rights Council in June 2018.[400] The US withdrew its membership from the UN Educational, Scientific, and Cultural Organization (UNESCO) on December 31, 2018.[401]

---

397 Jeff Stein, "Trump signs USMCA, revamping North American trade rules," *The Washington Post*, January 29, 2020.

398 Jim Tankersly, "Trump Signs Revised Korean Trade Deal," *The New York Times*, September 24, 2018.

399 Steve Holland and Lesley Wroughton, "Trump says NATO countries' burden-sharing improving, wants more," *Reuters*, April 2, 2019.

400 Colin Dwyer, "US Announces Its Withdrawal From U.N. Human Rights Council," *NPR*, June 19, 2018.

401 Eleanor Beardsley, "Critics Say US Withdrawing From UNESCO Allows Different Agendas to Surface," *NPR*, December 28, 2018.

The decisions to leave these two organizations relate to resolutions passed by both of them criticizing Israel.

Largely in response to perceived bias in the reporting on the current COVID-19 pandemic and allegations the organization covered up China's role early on, President Trump also cut funding for the World Health Organization (WHO) on May 29, 2020.[402] Rather than revise his position, President Trump also tends to push it further, doubling down on policy decisions. Because of this, he announced the US would be withdrawing from the WHO in July 2020, although it takes one year for the withdrawal to go into effect.[403]

The lack of US leadership, or even presence, in these global agreements and organizations does not mean they stop functioning. The leadership void has been filled, in large part, by China. In my chapter on General Secretary Xi Jinping's efforts to transform China's economy, focusing on developing new technology, I also touched on his desire to change global standards. He seeks to adjust standards that better protect the survival of the Chinese Communist Party (CCP) and other similar authoritarian regimes.

Ironically, China has benefitted greatly from the international trade norms and organizations established by the West. This includes membership in the UN and WTO for its development agenda. However, Xi Jinping seeks to not only make China independent from foreign technology companies but also to start writing the rules for global cyber governance.

---

402 Steve Holland and Michelle Nichols, "Trump cutting US ties with World Health Organization over virus," *Reuters*, May 29, 2020.

403 Emily Rauhala, Karoun Demirjian, and Toluse Olorunnipa, "Trump administration sends letter withdrawing US from World Health Organization over coronavirus response," *The Washington Post*, July 7, 2020.

Huawei and 5G play a key role in this effort. China is attempting to dominate high-speed wireless 5G networks globally. This leads to worries by US analysts and policymakers that China wants to set the standards for things like safety for these networks and that the Chinese government could use these networks to spy on other governments' secure information. 5G could be revolutionary for the future of technology because it supports countless other applications, including autonomous vehicles, with extremely fast wireless communications.

China has already started working on changing global standards related to personal privacy protection in the UN. These efforts could allow for authoritarian governments to repress civil liberties and to commit human rights abuses.[404]

Chinese companies, most notably Huawei and ZTE, sell video cameras equipped with facial recognition technology to countries all over the world. These countries include both democracies and authoritarian governments. Huawei's "Safe Cities" programs are ostensibly designed to assist police and security forces in their public safety and security efforts.[405] However, the technology is not regulated and could be used for things like spying on political rivals. Without a strong US presence in the discussions about these issues, China can gain enough support to pass resolutions protecting their companies that sell this technology.

---

404 Samm Sacks and Lorand Laskai, "China's Privacy Conundrum," *Slate*, February 7, 2019.

405 Jonathan E. Hillman and Maesea McCalpin, "Watching Huawei's 'Safe Cities'," *Center for Strategic and International Studies*, November 4, 2019.

MINOR POLICY CHANGES NEEDED AT HOME, MASSIVE STRATEGIC RE-THINKING NEEDED GLOBALLY

This chapter highlights the passion for autonomous vehicles demonstrated by people like Kevin Schlosser, who's heart-breaking personal story fuels him and DC-AVA to push for a safer driving future. Other organizations, such as organizations advocating for blind people or people with other physical disabilities, fight for the greater accessibility and freedom of mobility that autonomous vehicles could provide. Combining these different groups' efforts, such as the work done by CFM, is key to ensuring as many different people's voices are heard as possible. This combined effort presents the case, in advocating for autonomous vehicles, of a broad constituency of people who would benefit from their adaption in society.

Serving as the "Laboratories of Democracy," states perform a critical role serving as the testing ground for autonomous vehicles. These tests are necessary to decide which laws and safety standards work well, and which need to be adjusted. For those states that have yet to pass laws related to autonomous vehicles, plans such as the task force in the New Jersey state legislature provide a key arena for people both in the government and industry experts to discuss what should be in the law. States also demonstrate the amazing potential benefits autonomous vehicles could provide people if they have the proper regulations.

People in the autonomous vehicle industry do not want to drastically change the entire system for regulating vehicles in the US. Their aims are simply to achieve three basic points. They want to provide greater clarity on the existing standards created by NHTSA, to expand the number of exemptions until autonomous vehicles can be incorporated into the existing FMVSS framework, and to create an expedited path to be incorporated into the FMVSS. These goals may be simple to talk about but it remains up to the US House and Senate to create and pass laws that address these issues without weighing them down with unrelated partisan issues.

Regardless of who is the next president, there needs to be a major shift in America's foreign policy and diplomatic focus. The US needs these changes to both export autonomous vehicles to other countries and set the global standards related to them. Foreign policy and diplomacy in the twenty-first century doesn't resemble a simple game of checkers. In this analogy, moves are played out between one country and another one or two countries at a time. It is a game of chess. There are countless possible decisions to be made and both short and long term implications need to be considered. One mistake can set off a chain reaction which can damage a country's ability to achieve their desired policy outcome.

Greater cooperation between different groups of people produce a stronger result at the state and national levels. The same is true with respect to different countries working together to create standards and advance their mutual interests.

Therefore, the US needs to reassert its role as a leader in international institutions, such as the UN. It needs to rejoin organizations like the TPP which serve as a counterweight to Chinese economic influence in East Asia. The US also needs to rejoin the Paris Climate Accords to work for reducing GHG emissions with other countries. Ultimately, the US needs to be a part of any discussion about making global norms and standards in international bodies, whichever they may be. If not, it will be China, not the US, who will be making the rules related to human rights, the environment, and even autonomous vehicles.

The more different groups of people and different countries come together to develop autonomous vehicles, and promote the global standards for things like safety, the better the end result will be. Relations between China and the US are currently at their lowest point in probably forty years. The immediate future looks bleak for improvement. I hope I am wrong, however, because both countries have brilliant people and innovative companies working on autonomous vehicles.

Technology should be more cooperative to achieve the best possible solutions to problems. I hope the US wins the race for autonomous vehicles but it may be ten years or longer before the technology matures for passenger autonomous vehicles and hopefully much less for a policy framework at the national level. At the end of the day, I would be happy owning an autonomous vehicle made in China if it meant people like me would be able to own a car and drive again. But I would really love to own and drive an American-made autonomous vehicle!

CONCLUSION

Almost all of the many predictions now being made about 1996 hinge on the Internet's continuing exponential growth. But I predict the Internet will soon go spectacularly supernova and in 1996 catastrophically collapse."[406]

ROBERT METCALFE, FOUNDER OF 3COM, IN 1995

When asked about the Chinese government trying to censor the Internet. "Good luck. That's sort of like trying to nail Jello to the wall."[407]

BILL CLINTON, FORMER PRESIDENT OF THE UNITED STATES, IN 2000

406 Robert Strohmeyer, "The 7 Worst Tech Predictions of All Time," *ABC News*, December 31, 2008.

407 Bethany Allen-Ebrahimian, "The Man Who Nailed Jello to the Wall," *Foreign Policy*, June 29, 2016.

* * *

Trying to make a prediction about a new technology, particularly one as new and potentially revolutionary as the autonomous vehicle, can be very difficult. I hope the analysis I have provided in this book ages better than Robert Metcalf's prediction regarding the internet collapsing into irrelevance. The CCP has succeeded in "nailing Jello to the wall" but it took years and the cooperation of search engine sites like Baidu and thousands of staff to create and maintain the "Great Firewall."[408] Therefore, former President Clinton deserves the benefit of the doubt because even technology experts thought it was impossible to censor the internet.

In my introduction, I compared the race to develop autonomous vehicles to the lunar moon landing. I mentioned it would need the work of everyone, including engineers, technology experts, policymakers, and different government agencies all working together to develop and produce autonomous vehicles. For this book, I have talked to professors, engineers, people involved in the policymaking process at both the state and national level, strategic consultants, and people in the automotive industry. They are all working on the promotion and development of autonomous vehicles. Just like it takes a village to raise a child, it takes many different people to develop and produce a vehicle that drives itself.

In my interview with Dr. Sven Beiker, he described it is actually much bigger than sending a rocket to the moon and returning afterwards. He said, "This is much more like, how can we create a system? A living system, a sustainable system that requires much more than a couple of people. In

---

408 Ibid.

our case, a couple of vehicles." He said a more appropriate analogy would be to colonize the moon. This would require many different government departments. These departments would include the Department of Transportation, Department of Labor, Department of Commerce, and the Department of Justice.

With autonomous vehicles there is still a lot of uncertainty. There is still a lot to be worked out on the technology side, such as perfecting "sensor fusion" so autonomous vehicles can more accurately "perceive" the world around them. Companies also need to develop CPUs and GPUs, or series of these microchips, with more processing power to improve the system as a whole. A new technological device could also be created that could greatly improve the functioning of these vehicles. Cheaper equipment, like more affordable LiDAR sensors, would also help the industry's prospects for making these vehicles affordable.

Many new business and financial models have been proposed to make autonomous vehicles cheaper for consumers. However, these models are untested, and one, or all of them, could succeed or fail. Will Baidu's open-source Apollo project reduce costs by defraying the R&D costs between different partners, or will the partnership fall apart? Will Uber's new Fleits financial model allow them to operate a "robotaxi" fleet without actually owning any of the vehicles? Will Elon Musk and Professor X's efforts to forego LiDAR sensors in their vehicles really allow for level four or five autonomous driving? These models need to be tested to make sure safe autonomous vehicles will also be a commercially viable solution for companies to pursue.

It is in the political realm where I believe there is the most uncertainty. Will the US Congress be able to pass laws governing the safety of autonomous vehicles? Who will win the 2020 presidential election? Will this make any difference for the next, or current, president's policies concerning autonomous vehicles?

Will the Chinese government resist the urge to rely on SOEs? Wil the CCP's increasingly aggressive actions abroad cut off the supply chain for critical technology for autonomous vehicles, such as microchips?

Finally, how will the economic impacts of the COVID-19 pandemic influence both countries' political priorities for this new technology?

This book attempts to provide clarity on a number of these political issues, but there are still many more questions related to policy for autonomous vehicles.

I believe the next fight in the current US-China trade dispute will concern who sets the global standards for new technology. It has usually been taken as a guarantee the US would be the country to set these standards because they have been doing it for the last four decades.

Xi Jinping has made it clear that he wants that to change. China's efforts to include 5G networks in its BRI plans gives them leverage to gain the support of the recipient countries to create the standards for its practically limitless number of applications. However, China will have an uphill battle if it wants to win in this arena. It will be made easier if they are left unchallenged in international institutions. If the US decides to more forcibly challenge them, then China will need to work to gain the support of enough countries to overcome any American opposition.

Who will win the race between the US and China to develop and produce autonomous vehicles? If "winning" the race means who will be able to drive a vehicle autonomously first, then the US won that race back in the early DARPA Grand Challenges from 2004 to 2007. If the "winner" will be determined by who is able to deploy autonomous vehicles for large scale commercial purposes first, then China will have the advantage. Therefore, both of these countries have a "claim" to be the victor.

The economic and security tension between China and the US is not easing. There is a bifurcation in the two countries' technology sectors with both countries going in different directions. I think it will be more of a question of who wins where. The worst-case scenario is there will be "One Globe, Two Systems." I don't see either country letting the other country create one set of global standards.

China will likely win in China and developing countries like Asia, Africa, Eastern Europe, and parts of the Americas. Meanwhile, the US will likely win in the US, Europe, the rest of the Americas, and other allied countries like India, Japan, Australia, and South Korea.

If the worst-case scenario happens, two systems will emerge with two different sets of standards in these two "spheres." Hopefully these sets of standards will not be entirely incompatible, like Macintosh and Windows early on. If this happens, then the leaders of China and the US need to manage any technological challenges so that they do not spill over into other economic or security challenges.

One of the biggest problems with the current US-China trade dispute is the tension has closed down different avenues of communication. Greater communication would allow for both countries to resolve any disputes and prevent this "One Globe, Two Systems" scenario from taking place. It is in neither country's interests for economic and security tensions to continue. More, and not fewer, avenues of communication need to be established to come up with resolutions for these different concerns.

It is worth taking a step back from the tension and uncertainty of this technological competition between China and the US. Autonomous vehicles can offer incredible benefits to people in all countries. They offer the potential to drastically reduce traffic injuries and deaths. They can also provide greater freedom of mobility to people like me and millions of other blind, disabled, or elderly people. There are also numerous other commercial benefits, from short-range delivery to increased efficiency for long haul trucks. I sincerely hope that we can all enjoy our lives, benefitting from autonomous vehicles, sooner rather than later.

ACKNOWLEDGMENTS

Special thanks to the DC Autonomous Vehicles Association (DC-AVA) for all of the great outreach work they do for autonomous vehicles in the DC metro area. Thank you to the Association for Unmanned Vehicle Systems International (AUVSI) for granting me a media pass to attend the 2020 Automated Vehicles Symposium.

Special thanks go to the following people who pre-ordered my book and provided me with valuable revision suggestions during my revisions process as my Beta Reader Community: Lilya Greyson, Christopher Wilcox, Stuart Wilcox, Aly Aga, Mark Wilcox, Juliette Potter, Laura Wilcox, Simon Radford, Kevin Schlosser, Avi Kelin, Chris Schwarz, Brian Jee, Sven Beikier, Virind Gujral, Karolina Chachulska, David Kerrigan, Eric Koester, Rachel Lee, Clayton Keir, Zachary A. Karber, Christopher Dues, Byron Hughey, Hai-Vu Phan, Jan Halaska, Fabien Thayamballi, Stuart Pearson, Neil Chirite, Nima Veiseh, Cheri Stanton, Steve Stanton, Kymberly MacNeal, Joshua Brown, Carly DeBoer, Kai Phoenix Kuklinski, Nicholas Greenough, Jared Boddum, David Silbergeld, Will Smith, Zachary Olson, Corrina Liu, Uta Erdbruegger, Winifred R. Frost, Nicola Reeder, Erim Sarinoglu, Anna Masson, Pradeep

Thayamballi, Jeffrey Testani, Rose Carter, Richard Johnson, Anna Riegel, Dalton Dwyer, Sam Hyman, Vincent Lu, Tracy L Hughes, Stanley Drake, Sandra Sheiber, Susan Sheridan, Monica Boruch, Stanley Rosen, Nati Hurwitz Ivan Andreev Dragoun, Paul S. Orner, Francois Gatimu, Jaclyn Butler, Lord Walker, Todd Liipfert, Matthew McCoy, Clay Holk, Cory Fitz, Williams Sherry, Alexander Sanjenis, Eyal Aharoni, Vanessa Lane, Margarida Mendonca, Alexis Aronson, John Dougherty, Carol Day Young, Limeng Chen, Patrick Sullivan, Yunchu Wang, Joe McReynolds, Michael Kuebler, Grayson Slover, Dan Wang, Avy Mallik, Michael Jacko, Bradford Crist, Angelo Lan, Phil Hahn, William Georgia, Caroline Georgia, Lucas Chan, Brendan Travers, John S. Odell, Patricia Stanton-Brown, Alma Gildenhorn, David Liu, Christopher James Gisriel, Eamon Nolan, Andrew Devansky, Ming-min Yang, Sandy Moss, Katie Noethe-Moss, Tiffany Mosher, Judith Moss, Dustin Enlow, Kris Coombs, Sidney A Davidson, Meena Sebastian, Peter Sebastian, Dustin Parker, Florian Gross, Graham Keir, Chris Russo, Peter Nesbitt, Nicholas D'Souza, CHJ, William Kim, Ekaterina "Kate" Svyatets, and Randal Drew.

I'd like to finally thank those unnamed donors who chose to contribute anonymously.

APPENDIX

INTRODUCTION

Fox, Eva. "Education and Experience Will Help Americans Trust Self-Driving Cars," *Tesmanian*, May 20, 2020, https://www.tesmanian.com/blogs/tesmanian-blog/education-and-experience-will-help-americans-trust-self-driving-cars.

Hanes, Elizabeth. "From Sputnik to Spacewalking: 7 Soviet Space Firsts," *History Stories*. August 22, 2018. https://www.history.com/news/from-sputnik-to-spacewalking-7-soviet-space-firsts.

"Investment in China's smart cities to approach $39b by 2023," *China Daily*, July 14, 2019, https://www.chinadaily.com.cn/a/201907/14/WS5d2ad40ba3105895c2e7d51b.html.

Laris, Michael. "Trump administration proposed billions in transportation cuts – and new spending," *The Washington Post*, February 10, 2020, https://www.washingtonpost.com/local/trafficandcommuting/trump-administration-proposes-billions-in-transportation-cuts--and-new-spending/2020/02/10/85153096-4c5c-11ea-b721-9f4cdc90bc1c_story.html.

NASA. "July 20,1969: One Giant Leap For Mankind," *NASA Administrator*. Last modified July 20, 2019. https://www.nasa.gov/mission_pages/apollo/apollo11.html.

Wattanajantra, Asavin. "AI & Automation: benefits for business & industry," *Sage*, January 7, 2019, https://www.sage.com/en-us/blog/ai-automation-benefits-for-business-industry/.

Waymo. "2019 IAA Frankfurt Auto Show Remarks by John Krafcik." October 11, 2019. Video, 15:41. https://www.youtube.com/watch?v=qJiFKxvJlhY.

CHAPTER 2: FOR AUTONOMOUS VEHICLES, NECESSITY IS THE MOTHER OF INVENTION

"Autonomous vehicles cash in on coronavirus-driven demand," *hpauto*, May 18, 2020, https://auto.hindustantimes.com/auto/news/autonomous-vehicles-cashes-in-on-coronavirus-driven-demand-41589800756289.html.

"Delivering the future of local commerce, autonomously," *Nuro*, 2016, https://nuro.ai.

Fadulu, Lola. "Why is the US so Bad at Worker Retraining?," *The Atlantic*, January 4, 2018, https://www.theatlantic.com/education/archive/2018/01/why-is-the-us-so-bad-at-protecting-workers-from-automation/549185/.

Fishman, Ted C. "America's Next Crisis is Already Here," *The Atlantic*, May 21, 2020, https://www.theatlantic.com/ideas/archive/2020/05/state-and-local-governments-are-plunging-crisis/611932/.

Florida, Richard. "How Media Coverage of Car Crashes Downplays the Role of Driver," *Bloomberg CityLab*, December 10, 2019, https://www.bloomberg.com/news/articles/2019-12-10/why-news-coverage-of-car-crashes-favors-drivers.

Harwell, Drew."As Walmart turns to robots, it's the human workers who feel like machines," *The Washington Post*, June 6, 2019, https://www.washingtonpost.com/technology/2019/06/06/walmart-turns-robots-its-human-workers-who-feel-like-machines/.

Hawkins, Andrew J. "Nuro is using driverless robots to help health-care workers fighting COVID-19," *The Verge*, April 22, 2020, https://www.theverge.com/2020/4/22/21231466/nuro-delivery-robot-health-care-workers-food-supplies-california.

Holley, Peter. "Walmart teams with Nuro's robot cars to deliver groceries in Houston," *The Washington Post*, December 11, 2019, https://www.washingtonpost.com/technology/2019/12/11/walmart-teams-with-nuros-robot-cars-deliver-groceries-houston/.

John, Steven. "11 incredible facts about the $700 billion US trucking industry," *Business Insider*, June 3, 2019, https://markets.businessinsider.com/news/stocks/trucking-industry-facts-us-truckers-2019-5-1028248577#.

May, Melanie. "The 6 levels of self-driving car – and what they mean for motorists," TheJournal.ie, September 18, 2017, https://www.thejournal.ie/self-driving-cars-autonomy-levels-3603253-Sep2017/.

Moore, Michael. "AI investment will hit $232 billion by 2025," *ITProPortal*, July 31, 2018, https://www.itproportal.com/news/ai-investment-will-hit-dollar232-billion-by-2025/.

"National Center for Health Statistics," *The Center for Disease Control and Prevention*, 2017, https://www.cdc.gov/nchs/fastats/adolescent-health.htm.

Press Release, "INRIX: Congestion Costs Each American Nearly 100 Hours, $1,400 a year," *INRIX*, March 9, 2020, https://inrix.com/press-releases/2019-traffic-scorecard-us/.

Raphelson, Samantha. "Trucking Industry Struggles With Growing Driver Shortage," *Here & Now Compass*, January 9, 2018, https://www.npr.org/2018/01/09/576752327/trucking-industry-struggles-with-growing-driver-shortage.

SCDigest Editorial Staff, "Supply Chain News: MIT Report Says not to Expect Self-Driving Trucks any Time Soon," *Supply Chain Digest*, July 28, 2020, http://www.scdigest.com/ontarget/20-07-28_MIT_Autonomous_Trucking.php?cid=17022.

Templeton, Brad. "Where Robot Cars (Robocars) Can Really Take Us," *Bra Templeton's Home Page* (blog), https://www.templetons.com/brad/robocars/.

Wakabayashi, Daisuke. "Self-Driving Uber Car Kills Pedestrian in Arizona, Where Robots Roam," *The New York Times*, March 19, 2018, https://www.nytimes.com/2018/03/19/technology/uber-driverless-fatality.html.

CHAPTER 3: THE POTENTIAL POTHOLES AND ROADBLOCKS TO ACCEPTANCE OF AUTONOMOUS VEHICLES IN TH

Blanco, Sebastian. "Amazon Buys Autonomous Tech Company Zoox, and Elon Musk is Amused," *Car and Driver*, June 29, 2020, https://www.caranddriver.com/news/a33001491/amazon-buys-zoox-autonomous-company/.

"Cambridge research into driverless cars finds improved traffic flow," *BBC*, May 21, 2019, https://www.bbc.com/news/uk-england-cambridgeshire-48326428.

Davies, Andy. "An Oral History of the DARPA Grand Challenge, the Grueling Robot Race That Launched the Self-Driving Car," *Wired*, August 3, 2017, https://www.wired.com/story/darpa-grand-challenge-2004-oral-history/.

"Each Country's Share of CO2 Emissions," *Union of Concerned Scientists*, August 12, 2020, https://www.ucsusa.org/resources/each-countrys-share-co2-emissions.

Friedman, Lisa. "Trump Serves Notice to Quit Paris Climate Agreement," *The New York Times*, November 4, 2019, https://www.nytimes.com/2019/11/04/climate/trump-paris-agreement-climate.html.

Greenberg, Andy. "Hackers Remotely Kill a Jeep on the Highway – With Me In It," *Wired*, July 21, 2015, https://www.wired.com/2015/07/hackers-remotely-kill-jeep-highway/.

Greenberg, Andy. "The Jeep Hackers Are Back to Prove Car Hacking Can Get Much Worse," *Wired*, August 1, 2016, https://www.wired.com/2016/08/jeep-hackers-return-high-speed-steering-acceleration-hacks/.

Harvey, Fiona. "UN calls for push to cut greenhouse gas levels to avoid climate chaos," *The Guardian*, November 26, 2019, https://www.theguardian.com/environment/2019/nov/26/united-nations-global-effort-cut-emissions-stop-climate-chaos-2030.

Ingraham, Christopher. "Americans say there's not much appeal to to big-city living. Why do so many of us live there?," *The Washington Post*, December 18, 2018, https://www.washingtonpost.com/business/2018/12/18/americans-say-theres-not-much-appeal-big-city-living-why-do-so-many-us-live-there/.

Klebnikov, Sergei. "5 Big Numbers that Show Amazon's Explosive Growth During the Coronavirus Pandemic," *Forbes*, July 23, 2020, https://www.forbes.com/sites/sergeiklebnikov/2020/07/23/5-big-numbers-that-show-amazons-explosive-growth-during-the-coronavirus-pandemic/#70e0bc144137.

Kolkalitcheva, Kia. "People cause most California autonomous vehicle accidents," *Axios*, August 29, 2018, https://www.axios.com/california-people-cause-most-autonomous-vehicle-accidents-dc962265-c9bb-4b00-ae97-50427f6bc936.html.

Liao, Rita. "How China's first autonomous driving unicorn Momenta hunts for data," *Techrunch*, June 13, 2019, https://techcrunch.com/2019/06/13/momenta-profile/.

Schulman, Jeremy. “Every Insane Thing Donald Trump Has Said About Global Warming,” *Mother Jones*, December 12, 2018, https://www.motherjones.com/environment/2016/12/trump-climate-timeline/.

Skillman, Wendy. “Rare But Instructive Accidents Involving Autonomous Vehicles,” January 14, 2020, https://www.tysonmendes.com/rare-but-instructive-accidents-involving-autonomous-vehicles/.

Stromberg, Joseph. “The real story behind the demise of America’s once-mighty streetcar,” *Vox*, May 7, 2016, https://www.vox.com/2015/5/7/8562007/streetcar-history-demise.

Tabuchi, Hiroko. “How the Koch Brothers are Killing Public Transit Projects Around the Country,” *The New York Times*,” June 19, 2018, https://www.nytimes.com/2018/06/19/climate/koch-brothers-public-transit.html.

Teale, Chris. “Cities ‘finally waking up’ to the benefits of smart streetlights: survey,” *Smart Cities DIVE*, May 4, 2020, https://www.smartcitiesdive.com/news/survey-smart-streetlights-LED-northeast-group/577227/.

Templeton, Brad. "Where Robot Cars (Robocars) Can Actually Take Us,” *Brad Templeton Home*, https://www.templetons.com/brad/robocars/.

Vaughan, Adam. “US green economy has 10 times more jobs than the fossil fuel industry,” *NewScientist*, October 15, 2019, https://www.newscientist.com/article/2219927-us-green-economy-has-10-times-more-jobs-than-the-fossil-fuel-industry/.

Waymo, “2019 IAA Frankfurt Auto Show Remarks by John Krafcik,” October 11, 2019, video, 15:41, https://www.youtube.com/watch?v=qJiFKxvJlhY.

Woyke, Elizabeth. “The Blind Community Has High Hopes for Self-Driving Cars,” *MIT Technology Review*, October 12, 2016, https://www.technologyreview.com/2016/10/12/157034/the-blind-community-has-high-hopes-for-self-driving-cars/.

CHAPTER 4: VISION CORRECTION: IDENTIFYING THE BEST WAY FOR AUTONOMOUS VEHICLES TO “SEE” THE WORLD

“Bosch Unveils Lidar Sensor for Autonomous Driving,” *GIM International*, January 9, 2020, https://www.gim-international.com/content/news/bosch-unveils-lidar-sensor-for-autonomous-driving.

Brown, Mike. "LiDAR is Terrible for Self-Driving Cars, Says AutoX Founder," *Inverse*, April 18, 2017, https://www.inverse.com/article/29900-lidar-autox-founder-autonomous-cars.

Burns, Matt. "'Anyone relying on lidar is doomed, Elon Musk says," *TechCrunch*, April 22, 2019, https://techcrunch.com/2019/04/22/anyone-relying-on-lidar-is-doomed-elon-musk-says/.

Cameron, Oliver. "An Introduction to LIDAR: The Key Self-Driving Car Sensor," *Voyage*, May 9, 2017, https://news.voyage.auto/an-introduction-to-lidar-the-key-self-driving-car-sensor-a7e405590cff.

Cohen, Jeremy. "Sensor Fusion," *Towards Data Science*, May 22, 2018, https://towardsdatascience.com/sensor-fusion-90135614fde6.

Davies, Alex. "Waymo's Self-Driving Jaguar Arrives With New, Homewgrown Tech," *Wired*, March 4, 2020, https://www.wired.com/story/waymos-self-driving-jaguars-arrive-new-homegrown-tech/.

Davies, Chris. "A key part of many autonomous cars just got a huge pay cut," *Slash Gear*, January 2, 2018, https://www.slashgear.com/velodyne-lidar-puck-autonomous-car-more-affordable-02513340/.

"Innovusion Launches Image-Grade LiDAR System 'Cheeta'," *The Economic Times*, June 17, 2019, https://auto.economictimes.indiatimes.com/news/auto-technology/innovusion-launches-image-grade-lidar-system-cheetah/69828071.

Peng, Tony. "AutoX Wants to Put a Self-driving Car in Your Driveway in Two Years," *Synced*, September 12, 2017, https://medium.com/synced-review/autox-wants-to-put-a-self-driving-car-in-your-driveway-in-two-years-3395d68c4b80.

Rudgard, Olivia. "Self-driving cars will only last four years, Ford says," *The Telegraph*, August 25, 2019, https://www.telegraph.co.uk/technology/2019/08/25/self-driving-cars-will-last-four-years-ford-says/.

Stewart, Jack. "AutoX Slaps $50 Webcams on a Car to Make it Drive Itself," *Wired*, March 22, 2020, https://www.wired.com/2017/03/autox-slaps-50-webcams-car-make-drive/,

"The History of LIDAR," *Acroname*, January 16, 2020, https://acroname.com/blog/history-lidar.

Weber, Helko, Jorg Krings, Jonas Seyfferth, Hartmut Guthner, Jorn Neuhausen, et al. "The 2019 Strategy& Digital Auto Report," *Price-Waterhouse Cooper*, accessed February 23, 2020.

Yu, Yifan. "Professor X readies self-drive cars for China's busy streets," *Nikkei Asian Review*, August 23, 2019, https://asia.nikkei.com/Spotlight/Start-ups-in-Asia/Professor-X-readies-self-drive-cars-for-China-s-busy-streets.

Yvkoff, Liane. "Is Lidar Necessary for Self-Driving Cars? Audi Seems to Think So," *Forbes*, April 17, 2019, https://www.forbes.com/sites/lianeyvkoff/2019/04/17/is-lidar-necessary-for-self-driving-cars-audi-seems-to-think-so/#3b9e80df3acc.

CHAPTER 5: DISSECTING THE CENTRAL NERVOUS SYSTEM OF THE AUTONOMOUS VEHICLE

Angelini, Chris. "Security on the road: Locking down tomorrow's connected vehicles," *VentureBeat*, September 13, 2019, https://venturebeat.com/2019/09/13/security-on-the-road-locking-down-tomorrows-connected-vehicles/.

Anyoha, Rockwell. "The History of Artificial Intelligence," *Harvard University: The Graduate School of Arts and Sciences*, August 28, 2017, http://sitn.hms.harvard.edu/flash/2017/history-artificial-intelligence/.

Beltz, Brian. "100+ Car Accident Statistics for 2020," *Safer America*, October 25, 2018, https://safer-america.com/car-accident-statistics/.

Bergamini, Luca. Vladimir Iglovikov, Filip Hlasek, and Peter Ondruska. "Prediction Model for Autonomous Vehicles," *Lyft Level 5*, September 23, 2020, https://medium.com/lyftlevel5/how-to-build-a-motion-prediction-model-for-autonomous-vehicles-29f7f81f1580.

Burke, Katie. "How Do Self-Driving Cars Make Decisions?," *NVIDIA Blog*, May 7, 2019, https://blogs.nvidia.com/blog/2019/05/07/self-driving-cars-make-decisions/.

"Cerebral Cortex," *Brain Made Simple*, September 26, 2019, https://brainmadesimple.com/cerebral-cortex-and-lobes-of-the-brain/.

Dastin, Jeffrey. "Amazon scraps secret AI recruiting tool that showed bias against women," *Reuters*, October 9, 2018, https://www.reuters.com/article/us-amazon-com-jobs-automation-insight/amazon-scraps-secret-ai-recruiting-tool-that-showed-bias-against-women-idUSKCN1MK08G.

Davies, Alex. "An Oral History of the Darpa Grand Challenge, the Grueling Robot Race That Launched the Self-Driving Car," *Wired*, August 3, 2017, https://www.wired.com/story/darpa-grand-challenge-2004-oral-history/.

Davies, Alex. "The War to Remotely Control Self-Driving Cars Heats Up," *Wired*, March 26, 2019, https://www.wired.com/story/designated-driver-teleoperations-self-driving-cars/.

Deangelts, Stephen F. "Artificial Intelligence: How Algorithms Make Systems Smart," *Wired*, 2018, https://www.wired.com/insights/2014/09/artificial-intelligence-algorithms-2/.

Hao, Karen. "What is Machine Learning," *MIT Technology Review*, November 17, 2018, https://www.technologyreview.com/2018/11/17/103781/what-is-machine-learning-we-drew-you-another-flowchart/.

Hardesty, Larry. "Making driverless cars change lanes more like human drivers do," *MIT News*, May 22, 2018, https://news.mit.edu/2018/driverless-cars-change-lanes-like-human-drivers-0523.

Haydin, Victor. "How Machine Learning Algorithms Make Self-Driving Cars a Reality," *Intellias*, October 11, 2018, https://www.intellias.com/how-machine-learning-algorithms-make-self-driving-cars-a-reality/.

Horton, Mike. "IMU Technology Forms the Brains of the Autonomous Vehicle," *5G Technology World*, February 14, 2019, https://www.5gtechnologyworld.com/imu-technology-forms-the-brains-of-the-autonomous-vehicle/.

"Machine Learning Algorithms in Self-Driving Cars," *DexLab*, March 27, 2020, https://www.dexlabanalytics.com/blog/machine-learning-algorithms-in-self-driving-cars.

Matheson, Rob. "Study shows how fast humans react to road hazards," *MIT News*, August 7, 2019, https://news.mit.edu/2019/how-fast-humans-react-car-hazards-0807.

NorthEast Spine and Sports Medicine, "Important Nerves in the Body and What They Do," *Spine and Sports Medicine Blog*, May 8, 2020, https://www.northeastspineandsports.com/important-nerves-in-the-body-and-what-they-do/.

Rivelli, Elizabeth. "How Do Self-Driving Cars Work and What Problems Remain?," *The Simple Dollar*, June 30, 2020, https://www.thesimpledollar.com/insurance/auto/how-self-driving-cars-work.

Russell, Steve. "DARPA Grand Challenge Winner: Stanley the Robot," *Popular Mechanics*, January 9, 2006, https://www.popularmechanics.com/technology/robots/a393/2169012/.

Serieslove. "Child's Play (2019) – Chucky kills Doreen." October 13, 2019. Video, 2:46. https://www.youtube.com/watch?v=oPyOoHnxb1A.

Shale-Hester, Tristan. "Driverless cars will require one billion lines of code, says JLR," *Auto* Express, April 16, 2019, https://www.autoexpress.co.uk/car-news/106617/driverless-cars-will-require-one-billion-lines-of-code-says-jlr.

Steffora Mutschler, Ann. "Vehicle Communications Network is Due for Overhaul," *Semiconductor Engineering*, May 7, 2020, https://semiengineering.com/vehicle-communications-network-is-due-for-overhaul/.

Wood, Matt. "Area of brain associated with spatial awareness and planning action also plays crucial role in decision making," *University of Chicago Medicine*, July 10, 2019, https://www.uchicagomedicine.org/forefront/neurosciences-articles/posterior-parietal-cortex-plays-crucial-role-in-decision-making.

CHAPTER 6: JOHN KRAFCIK AND WAYMO: THE "BORING" COMPANY THAT LEADS THE RACE IN THE US

Beadham, Matthew. "Nearly 90% of Americans don't trust self-driving cars," *Shift*, March 6, 2010, https://thenextweb.com/shift/2020/03/06/nearly-90-of-americans-dont-trust-self-driving-cars/.

Davies, Alex. "Inside the Races That Jump-Started the Self-Driving Car," *Wired*, November 18, 2017, https://www.wired.com/story/darpa-grand-urban-challenge-self-driving-car/.

Franklin-Wallis, Oliver. "Inside X, Google's top-secret moonshot factory," *Wired*, February 17, 2020, https://www.wired.co.uk/article/ten-years-of-google-x.

"Google now testing self-driving cars in Washington," *MSNBC*, February 4, 2016, https://www.cnbc.com/2016/02/04/google-expands-self-driving-car-testing-to-washington-state.html.

Halsey III, Ashley. "Blind man sets out alone in Google's driverless car," *The Washington Post*, December 13, 2016, https://www.washingtonpost.com/local/trafficandcommuting/blind-man-sets-out-alone-in-googles-driverless-car/2016/12/13/f523ef42-c13d-11e6-8422-eac61c0ef74d_story.html.

Hartmans, Avery. "How Google's self-driving car project rose from a crazy idea to a top contender in the race toward a driverless future," *Business Insider*, October 23, 2016, https://www.businessinsider.com/google-driverless-car-history-photos-2016-10.

Kelly, Heather. "Google loses lead self-driving car engineer Chris Urnson," *CNN Business*, August 5, 2016, https://money.cnn.com/2016/08/05/technology/chris-urmson-google/.

Korasec, Kirsten. "Waymo to start selling standalone LiDAR sensors," *TechCrunch*, March 6, 2019, https://techcrunch.com/2019/03/06/waymo-to-start-selling-standalone-lidar-sensors/.

Krafcik, John. "John Krafcik," *LinkedIn*, August 25, 2020, https://www.linkedin.com/in/johnkrafcik/.

McFarland, Matt. "Waymo retires its cute self-driving car prototype," *CNN Business*, June 13, 2017, https://money.cnn.com/2017/06/13/technology/future/waymo-google-car-retired/index.html.

Naughton, Keith. "Waymo CEO sees driverless trucks catching on faster than taxis," *Automotive News Europe*, October 29, 2019, https://europe.autonews.com/automakers/waymo-ceo-sees-driverless-trucks-catching-faster-taxis.

Newcomb, Doug. "Google Hires Former Hyundai Exec John Krafcik as CEO of Self-Driving Car Project," *Forbes*, September 14, 2015, https://www.forbes.com/sites/dougnewcomb/2015/09/14/google-hires-former-hyundai-exec-john-krafcik-as-ceo-of-self-driving-car-project/#65319f2e6fac.

Onetto, Marc. "When Toyota met e-commerce: Lean at Amazon," *McKinsey & Company*, February 1, 2014, https://www.mckinsey.com/business-functions/operations/our-insights/when-toyota-met-e-commerce-lean-at-amazon.

Pressman, Aaron. "Waymo Reaches 20 Million Miles of Autonomous Driving," *Fortune*, January 7, 2020, https://fortune.com/2020/01/07/googles-waymo-reaches-20-million-miles-of-autonomous-driving/.

Reuters, "Here's Why Google Just Hired This Airbnb Exec," *Fortune*, August 28, 2016, https://fortune.com/2016/08/26/google-airbnb-self-driving-cars/.

Seung-heon, Park. "Hyundai and Kia Motors record 9% global market share," *Hani*, August 5, 2014, http://english.hani.co.kr/arti/english_edition/e_business/649906.html.

Slav, Irina. "Waymo logs in 20 million miles of self-driving," *Talking Biz News*, January 7, 2020, https://talkingbiznews.com/we-talk-biz-news/waymo-logs-in-20-million-miles-of-self-driving/.

Thibodeau, Ian. "Waymo to test self-driving cars on Novi roads," *The Detroit News*, October 26, 2017, https://www.detroitnews.com/story/business/autos/mobility/2017/10/26/waymo-winter-novi-tests/107021172/.

Undercoffler, David. "How I Made It: John Krafcik," *Los Angeles Times*, June 7, 2014, https://www.latimes.com/business/autos/la-fi-himi-john-krafcik-truecar-20140608-story.html.

Vasilash, Gary S. "Cars Without Coffee: When a Vehicle Isn't Driving Him, John Krafcik Takes the Porsche," *Auto Beat*, May 7, 2020, https://www.autobeatonline.com/articles/cars-without-coffee-when-a-vehicle-isnt-driving-him-john-krafcik-takes-the-porsche.

Wakabayashi, Daisuke. "Google's Parent Company Spins off Self-Driving Car Business," *The New York Times*, December 13, 2016, https://www.nytimes.com/2016/12/13/technology/google-parent-company-spins-off-waymo-self-driving-car-business.html.

Waymo. "2019 IAA Frankfurt Auto Show Remarks by John Krafcik." October 11, 2019. Video, 15:41. https://www.youtube.com/watch?v=qJiFKxvJlhY.

CHAPTER 7: UBER CREATES EITHER A REVOLUTIONARY NEW FINANCIAL MODEL OR A FLEIT OF FANCY

Bellairs, Richard. "What is ISO 26262? An Overview of ISO 26262 and ASIL," *Perforce*, January 3, 2019, https://www.perforce.com/blog/qac/what-is-iso-26262.

Belvedere, Matthew J. "'Moral compass' was off at Uber under co-founder Kolanick, says new CEO Dara Khosrowshahi," *CNBC*, January 23, 2018, https://www.cnbc.com/2018/01/23/uber-moral-compass-under-co-founder-kalanick-was-off-new-ceo-says.html.

Bensinger, Greg and Chester Dawson. "Toyota Investing $500 Million in Uber in Driverless-Car Pact," *Wall Street Journal*, August 27, 2018, https://www.wsj.com/articles/toyota-investing-500-million-in-uber-in-driverless-car-pact-1535393774.

Bosa, Deirdre. "Uber announces $1 billion investment into its self-driving car group, weeks before going public," *CNBC*, April 18, 2019, https://

www.cnbc.com/2019/04/18/uber-nabs-1-billion-self-driving-car-investment-from-softbank-others.html.

Cellan-Jones, Rory. "Uber's self-driving operator charged over fatal crash," *BBC*, September 16, 2020, https://www.bbc.com/news/technology-54175359.

Clifford, Catherine. "Uber's CEO: 'We are absolutely committed to self-driving cars," *MSNBC*, April 13, 2018, https://www.cnbc.com/2018/04/13/ceo-dara-khosrowshahi-uber-is-committed-to-self-driving-cars.html.

Conger, Kate. "Uber's Revenue Craters, as Deliveries Surge in Pandemic," *The New York Times*, August 6, 2020, https://www.nytimes.com/2020/08/06/technology/uber-ride-hailing-delivery-coronavirus.html.

Conger, Kate, Adam Satariano, and Michael de la Merced. "Just Eat Takeaway to Acquire Grubhub for $7.3 Billion," *The New York Times*, June 10, 2020, https://www.nytimes.com/2020/06/10/technology/uber-grubhub-just-eat.html.

De Vynck, Gerrit, Olivia Carville, and Lizette Chapman. "Uber's CEO, a Seasoned Dealmaker, Pursues His Biggest One Yet," *Bloomberg*, May 14, 2020, https://www.bloombergquint.com/business/uber-s-ceo-a-seasoned-dealmaker-pursues-his-biggest-one-yet.

Feiner, Lauren. "Uber stock falls after quarterly results bet estimates, but losses topped $1 billion," *CNBC*, November 4, 2019, https://www.cnbc.com/2019/11/04/uber-uber-q3-2019-earnings.html.

Gallen, Tim. "Arizona, Tempe sued by family of woman killed by self-driving Uber vehicle," *The Business Journals*, March 20, 2019, https://www.bizjournals.com/phoenix/news/2019/03/20/arizona-tempe-sued-by-family-of-woman-killed-by.html.

Griggs, Troy and Daisuke Wakabayashi. "How a Self-Driving Uber Killed a Pedestrian in Arizona," *New York Times*, Mach 21, 2018, https://www.nytimes.com/interactive/2018/03/20/us/self-driving-uber-pedestrian-killed.html.

Isaac, Mike, Erin Griffith, and Adam Satariano. "Uber Buys Postmates for $2.65 Billion," *The New York Times*, July 5, 2020, https://www.nytimes.com/2020/07/05/technology/uber-postmates-deal.html.

Kolodny, Lora. "Elon Musk is wrong on robotaxi timing, Uber CEO Dara Khosrowshahi says," *CNBC*, May 10, 2019, https://www.cnbc.com/2019/05/10/uber-ceo-dara-khosrowshahi-says-elon-musk-is-wrong-on-robotaxi-timing.html.

Laris, Michael. "'Raising the bar': Uber details shortcomings in self-driving car that killed pedestrian," *The Washington Post*, November 2, 2018, https://www.washingtonpost.com/local/trafficandcommuting/raising-the-bar-uber-details-shortcomings-in-self-driving-car-that-killed-pedestrian/2018/11/01/5152bc54-dd42-11e8-b3f0-62607289efee_story.html.

Lewis, Benjamin, Chris Mullen, Junko Yoshida, and Philip Koopman. "UL4600: Industry Approach and Applications." Panel discussion at the *2020 Automated Vehicle Symposium*. virtual, July 27, 2020. https://s36.a2zinc.net/clients/auvsi/avs2020/Public/SessionDetails.aspx?FromPage=Sessions.aspx&SessionID=3619&SessionDateID=57.

Marketing, "What is a REIT?," *Project Control*, December 1, 2018, http://projectcontrol-inc.com/2018/12/01/what-is-a-reit/.

Marshall, Aarian. "Uber and Waymo Abruptly Settle For $245 Million," *Wired*, July 9, 2018, https://www.wired.com/story/uber-waymo-lawsuit-settlement/.

Marshall, Aarian. "Why Wasn't Uber Charged in a Fatal Self-Driving Car Crash?," *Wired*, September 17, 2020, https://www.wired.com/story/why-not-uber-charged-fatal-self-driving-car-crash/.

McCausland, Phil. "Self-Driving Uber car that hit and killed woman did not recognize that pedestrians jaywalk," *NBC News*, November 9, 2019, https://www.nbcnews.com/tech/tech-news/self-driving-uber-car-hit-killed-woman-did-not-recognize-n1079281.

Plungis, Jeff. "What Uber's Fatal Self-Driving Crash Can Teach Industry and Regulators," *Consumer Report,*" November 19, 2019, https://www.consumerreports.org/car-safety/what-ubers-fatal-self-driving-crash-can-teach-industry-and-regulators/.

Root, Katie. "New Uber CEO may get $200 million," *TechCrunch*, August 28, 2017, https://techcrunch.com/2017/08/28/new-uber-ceo-may-get-200-million/.

SanGiovanni, Christopher, Ensar Becic, and Kristin Kingsley. "Lessons Learned from Uber Crash." Lecture presented at the *2020 Automated Vehicles Symposium*, virtual, July 27, 2020, https://s36.a2zinc.net/clients/auvsi/avs2020/Public/SessionDetails.aspx?FromPage=Sessions.aspx&SessionID=3612&SessionDateID=57.

Schwantes, Marcel. "Uber CEO Sent This Tweet After a Self-Driving Vehicle Killed a Pedestrian Today. Here's Where It Went Wrong," Inc.com, March 19, 2018, https://www.inc.com/magazine/202009/tom-foster/one-trust-kabir-barday-fastest-growing-company-2020-inc5000.html.

Somerville, Heather. "True price of an Uber ride in question as investors assess firm's value," *Reuters*, August 23, 2017, https://www.reuters.com/article/us-uber-profitability/true-price-of-an-uber-ride-in-question-as-investors-assess-firms-value-idUSKCN1B3103.

Stern, Ray. "Prosecutor: No Crime by Uber in Self-Driving Death; Crash Still Under Scrutiny," *Phoenix New Times*, March 8, 2019, https://www.phoenixnewtimes.com/news/uber-committed-no-crime-self-driving-crash-tempe-prosecutor-11231539.

Stewart, Ashley. "Evolution of a dealmaker: Expedia CEO Dara Khosrowshahi is PSBJ's Executive of the Year," *Puget Sound Business Journal*, December 9, 2016, https://www.bizjournals.com/seattle/news/2016/12/09/dara-khosrowshahi-expedia-ceo-dealmaker-profile.html.

Streitfeld, David and Nellie Bowles. "Uber's CEO Pick, Dara hosrowshahi, Steps Into Brighter Spotlight," *The New York Times*, August 28, 2017, https://www.nytimes.com/2017/08/28/technology/dara-khosrowshahi-uber-ceo.html.

"Uber picks Dara Khosrowshahi as its new boss," *The Economist*, September 2, 2017, https://www.economist.com/business/2017/09/02/uber-picks-dara-khosrowshahi-as-its-new-boss.

Zetlin, Minda. "Expedia Chief Dara Khosrowshahi Will Be Uber's Next CEO. Here's What We Know About Him," Inc.com, August 28, 2017, https://www.inc.com/minda-zetlin/expedia-chief-dara-khosrowshahi-will-be-ubers-next.html.

CHAPTER 8: IS ELON MUSK THE SAVIOR OR VILLAIN OF THE AUTONOMOUS VEHICLE INDUSTRY IN THE US?

Ausin, Shelbi. "10 Things You Didn't Know About Elon Musk," *US News*, May 23, 2018, https://www.usnews.com/news/national-news/articles/2018-05-24/10-things-you-didnt-know-about-elon-musk.

Brisbourne, Alex. "Tesla's Over-The-Air Fix: Best Example Yet of the Internet of Things?," *Wired*, May 25, 2018, https://www.wired.com/insights/2014/02/teslas-air-fix-best-example-yet-internet-things/.

Brown, Aaron. "Here's a look back at the Tesla car that started it all," *Business Insider*, March 30, 2016, https://www.businessinsider.com/tesla-roadster-history-2016-3.

Burns, Matt. "A Brief History of Tesla," *TechCrunch*, October 8, 2014, https://web.archive.org/web/20150717064829/https://techcrunch.com/gallery/a-brief-history-of-tesla/#/slide2.

Eisenstein, Paul A. "AAA study finds Americans are warming to electric vehicles, but most aren't ready to buy – at least not yet," *CNBC*, May 9, 2019, https://www.cnbc.com/2019/05/08/aaa-says-americans-warm-to-electric-cars-but-most-arent-ready-to-buy.html.

"Electric Vehicle Charging Network (Stations & Outlets): Charging a Cleaner Tomorrow," *much needed*, May 27, 2020, https://muchneeded.com/electric-vehicle-charging-network-statistics/.

"Elon Musk," Bibliography.com, May 26, 2020, https://www.biography.com/business-figure/elon-musk.

Gross, Daniel. "The Miracle of SolarCity," *Slate*, July 31, 2015, https://slate.com/business/2015/07/solarcity-the-company-didnt-invent-the-solar-panel-but-it-invented-something-even-more-important.html.

Hawkins, Andrew J. "How Tesla changed the auto industry forever," *The Verge*, July 28, 2017, https://www.theverge.com/2017/7/28/16059954/tesla-model-3-2017-auto-industry-influence-elon-musk.

Huffman, Connor. "How Well Does a Tesla Model 4 Work For a Long Trip?," *Car and Driver*, May 22, 2020, https://www.caranddriver.com/shopping-advice/a32081802/tesla-model-3-road-trip/.

Irfan, Umair. "Elon Musk's tweet about taking Tesla private has triggered a federal lawsuit," *Vox*, September 28, 2018, https://www.vox.com/2018/9/27/17911826/elon-musk-tesla-sec-twitter-lawsuit.

Kelly, Emre. "How Elon Musk took SpaceX from an idea to the cusp of making history," *USA Today*, May 26, 2020, https://www.usatoday.com/story/news/nation/2020/05/26/spacex-how-elon-musk-took-idea-cusp-history/5257977002/.

Klebnikov, Sergei. "8 Innovative ways Elon Musk Made Money Before He Was a Billionaire," *Everyday* Money, August 8, 2017, https://money.com/8-innovative-ways-elon-musk-made-money-before-he-was-a-billionaire/.

Kolodny, Lora. "Elon Musk sent a two-line email telling employees how great Tesla's autonomy day was, but it has lots of holes," *CNBC*, April 23, 2019, https://www.cnbc.com/2019/04/23/elon-musk-celebrates-flawed-tesla-autonomy-day-with-employee-email.html.

Kolodny, Laura and Michael Wayland. "Watch Tesla drivers apparently asleep at the wheel, renewing Autopilot safety questions," *CNBC*, September 9, 2019, https://www.cnbc.com/2019/09/09/watch-tesla-drivers-apparently-asleep-at-the-wheel-renewing-safety-questions.html.

Lambert, Fred. "Tesla Autopilot crash rate increases, but still lower than without Autopilot," *electrek*, January 16, 2020, https://electrek.co/2020/01/16/tesla-crashes-autopilot-increase-better-without-autopilot/.

Lassa, Todd. "Tesla Promises Full Level 5 by End of 2019, Model 3 Robotaxis by 2020," *Automobile*, April 23, 2019, https://www.automobilemag.com/news/tesla-autonomous-driving-level-5-model-3-robotaxi/.

Linnane, Clara. "Yes, Jack Dorsey, Elon Musk does have an idea about how to fix Twitter," *MarketWatch*, January 17, 2020, https://www.marketwatch.com/story/yes-jack-dorsey-elon-musk-does-have-an-idea-about-how-to-fix-twitter-2020-01-17.

Mac, Ryan, Mark Di Stefano, and John Paczkowski. "In a New Email, Elon Musk Accused a Cave Rescuer of Being a 'Child Rapist' and Says He 'Hopes' There's a Lawsuit," *BuzzFeed News*, September 4, 2018, https://www.buzzfeednews.com/article/ryanmac/elon-musk-thai-cave-rescuer-accusations-buzzfeed-email.

Matousek, Mark. "The most impressive things Tesla's cars can do in Autopilot," *Business Insider*, January 29, 2018, https://www.businessinsider.com/tesla-autopilot-functions-and-technology-2017-12.

O'Donovan, Caroline, Charlie Werzel, and Ryan Mac. "Elon Musk Has Always Been at War With the Media," *BuzzFeed News*, June 21, 2018, https://www.buzzfeednews.com/article/carolineodonovan/elon-musk-tesla-spacex-war-press-media.

O'Kane, Sean. "The message from Elon Musk's 'funding secured' mess is to never tweet," *The Verge*, August 7, 2019, https://www.theverge.com/tldr/2019/8/7/20758944/elon-musk-twitter-tesla-funding-secured-private-420.

Porter, Jon. "Tesla just made its one millionth car," *The Verge*, March 10, 2020, https://www.theverge.com/2020/3/10/21172895/tesla-one-million-cars-production-model-y.

Seedhouse, Erik. *SpaceX: Making Commercial Spaceflight a* Reality. New York: Praxis, June 15, 2013.

Stevens, Matt. "Why is Elon Musk Attacking the Media? We Explain. (Also, Give Us a Good Rating!)," *The New York Times*, May 24, 2018, https://www.nytimes.com/2018/05/24/business/elon-musk-tesla-twitter-media.html.

Stewart, Emily. "Elon Musk's week of pot smoking and wild emails, explained," *Vox*, September 8, 2018, https://www.vox.com/business-and-finance/2018/9/8/17834910/elon-musk-joe-rogan-podcast-tesla-stock.

"The full story of Thailand's extraordinary cave rescue," *BBC News*, July 14, 2018, https://www.bbc.com/news/world-asia-44791998.

Zanerhaft, Jaron. "Elon Musk: Patriarchs and Prodigies," *CSQ*, 2013, https://csq.com/2013/01/elon-musk-patriarchs-and-prodigies/#.XovqKi2z1yk.

Zaveri, Mihir. "Elon Musk Walks Back 'Pedo Guy' Attack on That Cave Diver," *The New York Times*, July 18, 2018, https://www.nytimes.com/2018/07/18/business/elon-musk-vern-unsworth-pedo-guy.html.

Zhou, Li. "Elon Musk and the Thai cave rescue: a tale of good intentions and bad tweets," *Vox*, July 18, 2018, https://www.vox.com/2018/7/18/17576302/elon-musk-thai-cave-rescue-submarine.

CHAPTER 9: THE DRAGON AWAKENS: XI JINPING LAYS THE PATH FOR CHINESE AUTONOMOUS VEHICLES

Branigan, Tania. "Xi Jinping vows to fight 'tigers' and 'flies' in anti-corruption drive," *The Guardian*, January 22, 2013, https://www.theguardian.com/world/2013/jan/22/xi-jinping-tigers-flies-corruption.

Carrico, Kevin. "I Mastered Xi Jinping Thought and I Have the Certificate to Prove It," *Foreign Policy*, October 18, 2018, https://foreignpolicy.com/2018/10/18/i-mastered-xi-jinping-thought-and-i-have-the-certificate-to-prove-it/.

Cheow, Eric Teo Chu. "Asian Security and the Reemergence of China's Tributary System," *The Jamestown Foundation*, September 16, 2004, https://jamestown.org/program/asian-security-and-the-reemergence-of-chinas-tributary-system/.

Cui, Hongyang. "Subsidy fraud leads to reform for China's EV market," *ICCT*, May 30, 2017, https://theicct.org/blogs/staff/subsidy-fraud-reforms-china-ev-market.

Dai, Sarah. "Baidu to build self-driving test facility in Chongqing as the Chinese city pushes ahead with smart city infrastructure," *South China Morning Post*, March 20, 2020, https://www.scmp.com/tech/big-tech/article/3076088/baidu-build-self-driving-test-facility-chongqing-western-city-pushes.

Desai, Umesh. "Huge investment in 'new infra' key to China's recovery," *Asia Times*, April 27, 2020, https://asiatimes.com/2020/04/huge-investment-in-new-infra-key-to-chinas-recovery/.

Doubek, James. "China Removes Presidential Term Limits, Enabling Xi Jinping to Rule Indefinitely," *NPR*, March 11, 2018, https://www.npr.org/sections/thetwo-way/2018/03/11/592694991/china-removes-presidential-term-limits-enabling-xi-jinping-to-rule-indefinitely.

Economy, Elizabeth. "History With Chinese Characteristics," *Foreign Affairs*, July/August 2017, https://www.foreignaffairs.com/reviews/review-essay/2017-06-13/history-chinese-characteristics.

Economy, Elizabeth C. *The Third Revolution: Xi Jinping and the New Chinese State*. New York: Oxford University Press, 2018.

Fiol-Mahon, Alexandra. "Xi Jinping's Anti-Corruption Campaign: The Hidden Motives of a Modern Day Mao," *Foreign Policy Research Institute*, August 17, 2018, https://www.fpri.org/article/2018/08/xi-jinpings-anti-corruption-campaign-the-hidden-motives-of-a-modern-day-mao/.

Grammaticas, Damian. "Chinese New President Xi Jinping: A man with a dream," *BBC News*, March 14, 2013, https://www.bbc.com/news/world-asia-china-21790384.

Ingram, Antony. "Has China 'Messe Up' Its Electric Car Charging Standards," *Green Car Reports*, July 24, 2014, https://www.greencarreports.com/news/1093467_has-china-messed-up-its-electric-car-charging-standards.

Kania, Elsa B. "Made in China 2025, Explained," *The Diplomat*, February 1, 2019, https://thediplomat.com/2019/02/made-in-china-2025-explained/.

Keller, Michael. "This is how road networks determine traffic capacity," *World Economic Forum*, November 22, 2019, https://www.weforum.org/agenda/2019/11/road-networks-determine-traffic-capacity-eth/.

Kerravala, Zeus. "What are data centers? How they work and how they are changing in size and scope," *Network World*, September 25, 2017, https://www.neworkworld.com/article/3223692/what-is-a-data-centerhow-its-changed-and-what-you-need-to-know.html.

Lungu, Andrei. "Interpreting the party's anti-corruption campaign," *RISAP*, September 27, 2017, http://risap.ro/en/interpreting-the-partys-anti-corruption-campaign/.

Marro, Nick, Hengrui Liu, and Yu Yan. "Opportunities and Challenges in China's Electric Vehicle Market," *China Business Review*, February 2, 2015, https://www.chinabusinessreview.com/opportunities-and-challenges-in-chinas-electric-vehicle-market/.

Mazzocco, Ilaria. "Electrifying: How China Built an EV Industry in a Decade," *Macro Polo*, July 8, 2020, https://macropolo.org/analysis/china-electric-vehicle-ev-industry/.

McBride, James and Andrew Chatzky. "Is 'Made in China 2025' a Threat to Global Trade?," *Council on Foreign Relations*, May 13, 2019, https://www.cfr.org/backgrounder/made-china-2025-threat-global-trade.

Mullin, Larry. "China's cities will soon be crawling with self-driving robotaxis," *Fast Company*, September 24, 2020, https://www.fastcompany.com/90553995/chinas-cities-will-soon-be-crawling-with-self-driving-robotaxis.

Ping, Chong Koh. "China's Xi Jinping stacks 25-member Politburo with loyalists," *Straits Times*, October 25, 2017, https://www.straitstimes.com/asia/east-asia/chinas-xi-stacks-25-member-politburo-with-loyalists.

Preen, Mark. "Economic Reform in China: Current Progress and Future Prospects," *China Briefing*, April 3, 2019, https://www.china-briefing.com/news/economic-reform-china-opening-up-future-prospects/.

Rappeport, Alan. "19th-Century 'Humiliation' Haunts China-US Trade Talks," *The New York Times*, March 27, 2019, https://www.nytimes.com/2019/03/27/us/politics/china-opium-wars-trade-talks.html.

Ruwitch, John. "Timeline – The rise of Chinese leader Xi Jinping," *Reuters*, March 16, 2018, https://www.reuters.com/article/us-china-parliament-xi-timeline/timeline-the-rise-of-chinese-leader-xi-jinping-idUSKCN1GS0ZA.

Shu, Catherine. "Autox launches its Robo Taxi service in Shanghai, competing with Didi's pilot program," *TechCrunch*, August 17, 2020, https://techcrunch.com/2020/08/16/autox-launches-its-robotaxi-service-in-shanghai-competing-with-didis-pilot-program/.

Stracqualursi, Veronica. "10 times Trump attacked China and its trade relations with the US," *ABC* News, November 9, 2017, https://abcnews.go.com/Politics/10-times-trump-attacked-china-trade-relations-us/story?id=46572567.

Sun, Yilei and Brenda Goh. "China wants new energy vehicle sales in 2025 to be 25% of all car sale," *Reuters*, December 7, 2019, https://www.reuters.com/article/us-china-autos-electric/china-wants-new-energy-vehicle-sales-in-2025-to-be-25-of-all-car-sales-idUSKBN1Y70BN.

Wu, Yuwen. "Profile: China's fallen security chief Zhou Yongkang," *BBC News*, October 12, 2015, https://www.bbc.com/news/world-asia-china-26349305.

Zhao, Suisheng. "The Belt and Road Initiative and Xi Jinping's foreign and domestic policy agenda," *The Asia Dialogue*, October 29, 2019, https://theasiadialogue.com/2019/10/29/the-belt-and-road-initiative-and-xi-jinpings-foreign-and-domestic-policy-agenda/.

CHAPTER 10: US-CHINA TRADE AND SECURITY TENSION COULD TURN THE CHINA DREAM TO A NIGHTMARE

Barreto, Elzko. "Alibaba IPO Is Officially the Biggest Ever at $25 Billion," *Business Insider*, September 22, 2014, https://www.businessinsider.com/alibaba-ipo-world-record-at-25-billion-2014-9.

Baynes, Chris. "Chinese police to use facial recognition technology to send jaywalkers instant fines by text," *Independent*, March 29, 2018, https://www.independent.co.uk/news/world/asia/china-police-facial-recognition-technology-ai-jaywalkers-fines-text-wechat-weibo-cctv-a8279531.html.

Buckley, Chris. "China Is Detaining Muslims in Vast Numbers. The Goal: 'Transformation.'," *The New York Times*, September 8, 2018, https://www.nytimes.com/2018/09/08/world/asia/china-uighur-muslim-detention-camp.html#.

Buckley, Chris and Keith Bradsher. "Brushing Aside Opponents, Beijing Imposes Security Law on Hong Kong," *The New York Times*, June 30,

2020, https://www.nytimes.com/2020/06/30/world/asia/china-critics-security-law-hong-kong.html.

"China Becomes Top Filer of International Patents in 2019 Amid Robust Growth for WIPO's IP Services, Treaties and Finances," *WIPO*, April 7, 2020, https://www.wipo.int/pressroom/en/articles/2020/article_0005.html.

Coletta, Amanda. "Canadian court rules extradition case against Huawei executive Meng Wanzhou can proceed," *The Washington Post*, May 27, 2020, https://www.washingtonpost.com/world/the_americas/huawei-meng-wanzhou-canada-extradition/2020/05/27/8305b676-9f87-11ea-be06-af5514ee0385_story.html.

Earley, Kelly. "AutoX raises $100m from Dongfeng Motor and Alibaba," *Silicon Republic*, September 17, 2019, https://www.siliconrepublic.com/start-ups/autox-funding-alibaba-dongfeng-motor.

"Exclusive interview of Huawei founder Ren Zhengfei: Technology competition is peaceful game," *CGTN*, January 21, 2019, https://news.cgtn.com/news/3d3d514d7959544d32457a6333566d54/index.html.

Fifield, Anna. "'Bloodthirsty' like a wolf: Inside the military-style discipline at China's tech titan, Huawei," *The Washington Post*, December 13, 2018, https://www.washingtonpost.com/world/asia_pacific/bloodthirsty-like-a-wolf-inside-the-military-style-discipline-at-chinas-tech-titan-huawei/2018/12/12/76055116-fd85-11e8-a17e-162b712e8fc2_story.html.

Flamm, Kenneth. "Coping With Globalization in Semiconductors," *World Politics Review*, June 15, 2010, https://www.worldpoliticsreview.com/articles/5795/coping-with-globalization-in-semiconductors.

Frisch, Nick. "We Should Worry About How China Uses Apps Like TikTok," *The New York Times*, May 2, 2019, https://www.nytimes.com/interactive/2019/05/02/opinion/will-china-export-its-illiberal-innovation.html.

Geller, Eric. "Trump signs order setting stage to ban Huawei from the US," *Politico*, May 15, 2010, https://www.politico.com/story/2019/05/15/trump-ban-huawei-us-1042046.

Hansler, Jennifer. Nicole Gaouette, and Kylie Atwood, "Pompeo says Hong Kong is no longer autonomous from China, jeopardizing billions of dollars in trade," *CNN*, May 27, 2020, https://www.cnn.com/2020/05/27/politics/hong-kong-pompeo-certification/index.html.

Herwitz, Josh. "Why the semiconductor is suddenly at the heart of US-China tech tension," *Quartz*, July 24, 2018, https://qz.com/1335801/us-china-tech-why-the-semiconductor-is-suddenly-at-the-heart-of-us-china-tensions/.

"Huawei founder Ren Zhengfei denies firm poses spying risk," *BBC News*, January 15, 2019, https://www.bbc.com/news/technology-46875747.

Ihara, Kensaku. "Taiwan loses 3,000 chip engineers to 'Made in China 2025,'" *Nikkei Asian Review*, December 3, 2019, https://asia.nikkei.com/Business/China-tech/Taiwan-loses-3-000-chip-engineers-to-Made-in-China-2025.

Keane, Sean. "Huawei ban timeline: India will reportedly phase Huawei gear out as border tensions rise," *cnet*, August 25, 2020, https://www.cnet.com/news/huawei-ban-full-timeline-us-restrictions-china-trump-executive-order-android-google-ban/.

Kharpal, Arjun. "Trump 'apoplectic' with U.K. over Huawei 5G decision as US suggests taking stake in Nokia, Ericsson," *CNBC*, February 7, 2020, https://www.cnbc.com/2020/02/07/us-should-take-stake-in-nokia-ericsson-to-counter-huawei-in-5g-barr.html.

Kong, Leelian. "What Jack Ma can teach international students about learning English," *Study International News*, June 25, 2018, https://www.studyinternational.com/news/what-jack-ma-can-teach-international-students-about-learning-english/.

Leonard, Jenny, Enda Curran, and Bloomberg. "How the US-China Trade war Has Reached a Turning Point," *Fortune*, April 17, 2019, https://fortune.com/2019/04/17/trump-trade-war-us-china-talks/.

Liu, Andrew. "An Analysis of the PBOC's New Mobile Payment Regulation," *Winter 2019 Cato Journal*, 2019, https://www.cato.org/cato-journal/winter-2019/analysis-pbocs-new-mobile-payment-regulation.

Ma, Jack. "Jack Ma: 'Harvard rejected me 10 times,'" *World Economic Forum*, September 14, 2015, https://www.weforum.org/agenda/2015/09/jack-ma-harvard-rejected-me-10-times/.

Popovic, Stevan. "Jack Ma: The man leading the Chinese e-commerce market," *Hot Topics*, May 4, 2014, https://www.hottopics.ht/3885/jack-ma-the-man-leading-the-chinese-e-commerce-market/.

Qualcomm. "Everything you need to know about 5G." *Research & Invention*. Last modified 2020. https://www.qualcomm.com/invention/5g/what-is-5g?gclid=CjoKCQjwy8f6BRC7ARIsAPIXOjiBBIvydPPVGaDEXh4DIuHJerf3CBOuh8xV56k3K45AuWvrn1vMk-saAkemEALw_wcB.

Rogers, Adam. "US Accuses Chinese Company of Stealing Micron Trade Secrets," *Wired*, November 1, 2018, https://www.wired.com/story/us-accuses-chinese-stealing-micron-trade-secrets/.

Rose, Charlie. "Charlie Rose Talks to Alibaba's Jack Ma," *Bloomberg Businessweek*, January 29, 2015, https://www.bloomberg.com/news/articles/2015-01-29/alibaba-s-jack-ma-on-early-obstacles-his-ambitions.

Sin, Noah and Tom Westbrook. "Hong Kong stocks fal most since 2015 as Beijing pushes security law," *Reuters*, May 22, 2020, https://www.reuters.com/article/hongkong-markets/hong-kong-stocks-fall-most-since-2015-as-beijing-pushes-security-law-idUSAZN18OWoo.

Soo, Zen and Li Tao. "How Alibaba's Taobao solved the trust problem in China and changed the way people shop," *South China Morning Post*, August 24, 2018, https://www.scmp.com/tech/enterprises/article/2161082/how-alibabas-taobao-solved-trust-problem-china-and-changed-way.

Tiezzi, Shannon. "What did China Accomplish at the Belt and Road Forum?," *The Diplomat*, May 16, 2017, https://thediplomat.com/2017/05/what-did-china-accomplish-at-the-belt-and-road-forum/.

Wang, Helen H. "Alibaba Sage III: Jack Ma Discovered the Internet," *Forbes*, July 17, 2014, https://www.forbes.com/sites/helenwang/2014/07/17/alibaba-saga-iii/#169978f63058.

Xiao, Yan. "How digital payments can help countries cope with COVID-19, other pandemics: Lessons from China," *World Economic Forum*, May 6, 2020, https://www.weforum.org/agenda/2020/05/digital-payments-cash-and-covid-19-pandemics/.

CHAPTER 11: ROBIN LI AND BAIDU'S OPEN SOURCE APOLLO PROJECT: PROPHECY OR RECIPE FOR DISASTER?

Altucher, James. "10 Unsurprising Things About Google (also: the worst VC decision I ever made)," *Forbes*, March 18, 2011, https://www.forbes.com/sites/jamesaltucher/2011/03/18/10-unusual-things-about-google-also-the-worst-vc-decision-i-ever-made/#52034ad412ee.

Ancarola, Gabi. "The Tragic Story of the Fall of Icarus," *Greek Reporter*, April 17, 2018, https://greece.greekreporter.com/2018/04/17/the-tragic-story-of-the-fall-of-icarus/.

Baidu. "How coronavirus is accelerating a future with autonomous vehicles," *MIT Technology Review*, May 18, 2020, https://www.technologyreview.com/2020/05/18/1001760/how-coronavirus-is-accelerating-autonomous-vehicles/.

Barboza, David. "The Rise of Baidu (That's Chinese for Google)," *The New York Times*, September 17, 2006, https://www.nytimes.com/2006/09/17/business/yourmoney/17baidu.html.

Carrillo, Azahara Benito. "Why Internet users in China prefer Baidu over Google," *via firma*, February 14, 2019, https://www.viafirma.com/blog-xnoccio/en/china-prefer-baidu/.

Cartwright, Mark. "Apollo," *Ancient History Encyclopedia*, July 25, 2019, https://www.ancient.eu/apollo/.

Gandolfo, Ryan. "Baidu Leading the Way for Autonomous Driving in China," *that's Beijing*, November 5, 2018, https://www.thatsmags.com/beijing/post/25654/baidu-leading-the-way-for-autonomous-driving-in-china.

Lee, Kai-fu. *AI Sperpowers: China, Silicon Valley, and the New World Order.* New York. Houghton Mifflin Harcourt, 2018.

Li, Yanhong. "Towards a Qualitative Search Engine." *IEEE Internet Computing*, vol. 2, no. 4, pp. 24-29. July/August 1998, https://ieeexplore.ieee.org/document/707687.

Miller, Paul. "Baidu's 'Little Fish' home robot could be China's Echo," *The Verge*, January 5, 2017, https://www.theverge.com/circuitbreaker/2017/1/5/14178414/baidu-robot-duer-os-china.

Olazo, Jillian. "Baidu, China Unicom embark on AI partnership," *S&P Global*, November 3, 2016, https://www.spglobal.com/marketintelligence/en/news-insights/trending/KT_mcs5t7_-7ZwQx--3iNw2.

Parker, Garrett. "10 Things You Didn't Know About Baidu Founder Robin Li," *Money, Inc.*, visited September 8, 2020, https://moneyinc.com/10-things-didnt-know-baidu-founder-robin-li/.

Qiu, Yuxian. "Baidu Apollo Leads Self-Driving Advances," *Equal Ocean*, July 3, 2019, https://equalocean.com/news/2019070311298.

"Robin Li's vision powers Baidu's Internet search dominance," *Taipei Times*, September 17, 2006, http://www.taipeitimes.com/News/bizfocus/archives/2006/09/17/2003328060.

"Search Engine Market Share China," *GlobalStats*, August 2020, https://gs.statcounter.com/search-engine-market-share/all/china.

Sheehan, Matt. "How Google took on China – and lost," *MIT Technology Review*, December 19, 2018, https://www.technologyreview.com/2018/12/19/138307/how-google-took-on-china-and-lost/.

Shen, Jill. "Baidu is building everything Chongqing needs for self-driving cars," *technode*, March 20, 2020, https://technode.com/2020/03/20/baidu-is-building-everything-chongqing-needs-for-self-driving-cars/.

Wang, Xiaowei. "How Baidu maps turn location data into 3-D cityscapes – and big profits," *The Architect's Newspaper*, May 17, 2019, https://www.archpaper.com/2019/05/baidu-maps-tech-print/.

Watts, Jonathan. "The man behind China's answer to Google: accused by critics of piracy and censorship," *The* Guardian, December 9, 2005, https://www.theguardian.com/technology/2005/dec/08/piracy.news.

Wiggers, Kyle. "77 autonomous vehicles drove over 500,000 miles across Beijing in 2019," *Ventura Beat*, March 2, 2020, https://venturebeat.com/2020/03/02/77-autonomous-vehicles-drove-over-500000-miles-across-beijing-in-2019/.

Wiggers, Kyle. "Baidu announces Apollo 3.5 and Apollo Enterprise, says it has over 130 partners," *Venture Beast*, January 8, 2019, https://venturebeat.com/2019/01/08/baidu-announces-apollo-3-5-and-apollo-enterprise-says-it-has-over-130-partners/.

Zhang, Yufy. "Apollo: China's Autonomous Driving Program Explained," *EE Times Asia*, June 21, 2018, https://www.eetasia.com/18062105-apollo-chinas-autonomous-driving-program/.

CHAPTER12: PROFESSOR X AND AUTOX: "DEMOCRATIZING" AUTONOMOUS DRIVING

Chovanec, Megan. "My grandma's Los Altos garage is where Apple was created," *Business Insider*, January 31, 2015, https://www.businessinsider.com/my-grandmas-los-altos-garage-is-where-apple-was-created-2015-1.

Ho, Chua Kong and Sarah Dai. "China's Professor X says we are at the tipping point for mass roll-out of self-driving cars after tech advances," *South China Morning Post*, September 11, 2019, https://www.scmp.com/tech/innovation/article/3026544/chinas-professor-x-says-we-are-tipping-point-mass-roll-out-self.

"Jianxiong Xiao," *Credit Suisse*, March 28, 2020, https://www.credit-suisse.com/microsites/conferences/aic/en/speakers/speakers/jianxiong-xiao.html.

Larson, Christina. "The Big Test," *Foreign Policy*, June 10, 2011, https://foreignpolicy.com/2011/06/10/the-big-test/.

Lin, Qiqing. "'996' is China's Version of Hustle Culture. Tech Workers Are Sick of It.," *The New York Times*, April 29, 2019, https://www.nytimes.com/2019/04/29/technology/china-996-jack-ma.html.

Metz, Rachel. "AutoX Has Built a Self-Driving Car That Navigates With a Bunch of $50 Webcams," *MIT Technology Review*, March 28, 2017, https://www.technologyreview.com/2017/03/28/152924/autox-has-built-a-self-driving-car-that-navigates-with-a-bunch-of-50-webcams/.

Peng, Tony. "AutoX Wants to Put a Self-Driving Car in Your Driveway in Two Years," *Synced*, September 12, 2017, https://syncedreview.com/2017/09/12/autox-wants-to-put-a-self-driving-car-in-your-driveway-in-two-years/.

PoN Staff, "The Importance of Relationship Building in China," *Harvard Law School: Program on Negotiations Daily Blog*, October 14, 2019, https://www.pon.harvard.edu/daily/international-negotiation-daily/negotiation-in-china-the-importance-of-guanxi/.

Shu, Catherine. "AutoX launches its RoboTaxi service in Shanghai, competing against Didi pilot program," *TechCrunch*, August 17, 2020, https://techcrunch.com/2020/08/16/autox-launches-its-robotaxi-service-in-shanghai-competing-with-didis-pilot-program/.

Xiao, Jianxiong. "Democratizing Autonomous Driving." March 27, 2017. *MIT Technology Review*, Massachusetts Institute of Technology. speech, 32:10. https://events.technologyreview.com/video/watch/jianxiong-xiao-autoxinc-autonomous-driving/.

Xiao, Jianxiong. "Jianxiong Xiao (Professor X)," jianxiongxiao.com, visited June 7, 2020, http://www.jianxiongxiao.com.

Yu, Yifan. "Professor X readies self-drive cars for China's busy streets," *Nikkei Asian Review*, August 23, 2019, https://asia.nikkei.com/Spotlight/Startups-in-Asia/Professor-X-readies-self-drive-cars-for-China-s-busy-streets.

CHAPTER 13: POLICIES NEEDED TO PAVE THE WAY FOR AN AUTONOMOUS VEHICLES VICTORY FOR THE US

Alper, Alexandra and Timothy Gardner. "Trump promotes pulling US from Paris climate accord in speech touting 'America First'," *Reuters*, October 23, 2019, https://www.reuters.com/article/us-usa-trump-energy/trump-to-promote-withdrawing-u-s-from-paris-climate-accord-source-idUSKBN1X22F4.

"Autonomous Vehicles," *GHSA*, visited September 10, 2020, https://www.ghsa.org/state-laws/issues/autonomous%20vehicles.

Beardsley, Eleanor. "Critics Say US Withdrawing From UNESCO Allows Different Agendas to Surface," *NPR*, December 28, 2018, https://www.npr.org/2018/12/28/680616404/critics-say-u-s-withdrawal-from-unesco-allows-different-agendas-to-surface.

Beene, Ryan. "Bipartisan Autonomous Vehicle Legislation Stalls on Capital Hill," *Insurance Journal*, November 2, 2018, https://www.insurancejournal.com/news/national/2018/11/02/506418.htm.

Blakeman, Bradley A. "States are the laboratories of democracy," *The Hill*, May 7, 2020, https://thehill.com/opinion/judiciary/496524-states-are-the-laboratories-of-democracy.

Blumenthal, Richard. Twitter Post. April 3, 2018, 3:51p.m. https://twitter.com/SenBlumenthal/status/981257797269688321.

"Coalition Members," *Coalition for Future Mobility*, visited September 10, 2020, https://coalitionforfuturemobility.com/members/.

Dwyer, Colin. "US Announces Its Withdrawal From U.N. Human Rights Council," *NPR*, June 19, 2018, https://www.npr.org/2018/06/19/621435225/u-s-announces-its-withdrawal-from-u-n-s-human-rights-council.

"Federal Motor Vehicle Safety Standards and Regulations," *Department of Transportation*, March 1, 1967, https://one.nhtsa.gov/cars/rules/import/FMVSS/index.html.

Fletcher, Bevin. "FCC looks to dedicate 5.9GHz for Wi-Fi, C-V2X use," *Fierce Wireless*, November 20, 2019, https://www.fiercewireless.com/regulatory/fcc-looks-to-dedicate-5-9-ghz-for-wi-fi-c-v2x-use.

Hazzard, Tracy. "'How to Become the Center of Influence Through Podcasting and Validating Niche Expertise' with Marc Hoag of Autonomous Cars," *Authority Magazine*, May 15, 2019, https://medium.com/authority-magazine/how-to-become-the-center-of-influence-through-podcasting-and-validating-niche-expertise-with-bfa9e9586fea.

Hillman, Jonathan E. and Maesea McCalpin. "Watching Huawei's 'Safe Cities'," *Center for Strategic and International Studies*, November 4, 2019, https://www.csis.org/analysis/watching-huaweis-safe-cities.

Holland, Steve and Lesley Wroughton. "Trump says NATO countries' burden-sharing improving, wants more," *Reuters*, April 2, 2019, https://www.reuters.com/article/us-usa-nato-trump/trump-says-nato-countries-burden-sharing-improving-wants-more-idUSKCN1RE23P.

Holland, Steve and Michelle Nichols. "Trump cutting US ties with World Health Organization over virus," *Reuters*, May 29, 2020, https://www.reuters.com/article/us-health-coronavirus-trump-who/trump-cutting-u-s-ties-with-world-health-organization-over-virus-idUSKBN2352YJ.

Johnson, Jenna. "What does 'America first' really mean?," *The Washington Post*, April 27, 2018, https://www.washingtonpost.com/politics/what-does-america-first-really-mean/2018/04/25/907d2964-46ed-11e8-9072-f6d4bc32f223_story.html.

Karsten, Jack and Darrell West. "The state of self-driving car laws across the US," *Brookings Institute*, May 1, 2018, https://www.brookings.edu/blog/techtank/2018/05/01/the-state-of-self-driving-car-laws-across-the-u-s/.

Killinger, Jennifer. "ACC Joins Coalition for Future Mobility," *American Chemistry Council*, April 1, 2019, https://www.americanchemistry.com/Media/PressReleasesTranscripts/RelatedPDF/ACC-Joins-Coalition-for-Future-Mobility.pdf.

Landler, Mark. "Trump Abandons Iran Nuclear Deal He Long Scorned," *The New York Times*, May 8, 2018, https://www.nytimes.com/2018/05/08/world/middleeast/trump-iran-nuclear-deal.html.

Rauhala, Emily, Karoun Demirjian, and Toluse Olorunnipa. "Trump administration sends letter withdrawing US from World Health Organization over coronavirus response," *The Washington Post*, July 7, 2020, https://www.washingtonpost.com/world/trump-united-states-withdrawal-world-health-organization-coronavirus/2020/07/07/ae0a25e4-b550-11ea-9a1d-d3db1cbe07ce_story.html.

Roberts, Chris and Kevin Schlosser. "How Policy Drives the Future of Autonomous Vehicles," *D.C. Autonomous Vehicles Association*, May 12, 2020, https://www.meetup.com/DC-Autonomous-Vehicles-Association/events/270387624/.

Sacks, Samm and Lorand Laskai. "China's Privacy Conundrum," *Slate*, February 7, 2019, https://slate.com/technology/2019/02/china-consumer-data-protection-privacy-surveillance.html.

Scribner, Marc. "Congress Must Help Modernize Outdated Auto Safety Regulations," *Competitive Enterprise Institute*, January 9, 2018, https://cei.org/blog/congress-must-help-modernize-outdated-auto-safety-regulations.

Shepardson, David. "Self-driving car advocates launch ad campaign to prod Congress," *Reuters*, September 26, 2017, https://www.reuters.com/article/us-autos-selfdriving/self-driving-car-advocates-launch-ad-campaign-to-prod-congress-idUSKCN1C114F.

Shinkle, Doug. "Crafting Inclusive Autonomous Vehicle Policies," *Our American States*, April 3, 2020, https://www.ncsl.org/research/transportation/crafting-inclusive-autonomous-vehicle-policies.aspx.

Stein, Jeff. "Trump signs USMCA, revamping North American trade rules," *The Washington Post,* January 29, 2020, https://www.washingtonpost.com/business/2020/01/29/trump-usmca/.

Stumpf, Rob. "Trump Wants Nothing to Do With 'Crazy' Driverless Cars," *The Drive*, March 18, 2019, https://www.thedrive.com/news/27003/trump-wants-nothing-to-do-with-crazy-driverless-cars-report.

Tankersly, Jim. "Trump Signs Revised Korean Trade Deal," *The New York Times*, September 24, 2018, https://www.nytimes.com/2018/09/24/us/politics/south-korea-trump-trade-deal.html.

Taylor, Adam. "A timeline of Trump's complicated relationship with the TPP," *The Washington Post*, April 13, 2018, https://www.washingtonpost.com/news/worldviews/wp/2018/04/13/a-timeline-of-trumps-complicated-relationship-with-the-tpp.

CONCLUSION

Allen-Ebrahimian, Bethany. "The Man Who Nailed Jello to the Wall," *Foreign Policy*, June 29, 2016, https://foreignpolicy.com/2016/06/29/the-man-who-nailed-jello-to-the-wall-lu-wei-china-internet-czar-learns-how-to-tame-the-web/.

Strohmeyer, Robert. "The 7 Worst Tech Predictions of All Time," *ABC News*, December 31, 2008, https://abcnews.go.com/Technology/PCWorld

CPSIA information can be obtained
at www.ICGtesting.com
Printed in the USA
BVHW090610211220
596044BV00006B/14